S

F*CK DRUGS

Take Control of Your Life and Become Completely Drug-Free in 30 Days + Drug Addiction Recovery Success Story

By

Elliott J. Power

Legal & Disclaimer

The information contained in this book and its contents is not designed to replace or take the place of any form of medical or professional advice. It is not meant to replace the need for independent medical, financial, legal, or other professional advice or services, as may be required. The content and information in this book have been provided for educational and entertainment purposes only.

The content and information contained in this book have been compiled from sources deemed reliable, and it is accurate to the best of the Author's knowledge, information, and belief. However, the author cannot guarantee its accuracy and validity and cannot be held liable for any errors and omissions. Further, changes are periodically made to this book as and when needed. Where appropriate and necessary, you must consult a professional (including but not limited to your doctor, attorney, financial advisor, or such other professional advisor) before using any of the suggested remedies, techniques, or information in this book.

Upon using the contents and information contained in this book, you agree to hold harmless the Author from and against any damages, costs, and expenses, including any legal fees potentially resulting from the application of any of the information provided by this book. This disclaimer applies to any loss, damages or injury caused by the use and application, whether directly or indirectly, of any advice or information presented, whether for breach of contract, tort, negligence, personal injury, criminal intent, or under any other cause of action.

You agree to accept all risks of using the information presented inside this book.

You agree that by continuing to read this book, where appropriate and necessary, you shall consult a professional (including but not limited to your doctor, attorney, or financial advisor or such other advisor as needed) before using any of the suggested remedies, techniques, or information in this book.

Thanks again for choosing this book, make sure to leave a short review on Audible if you enjoy it. I'd really love to hear your thoughts.

CHAPTER 1
INTRODUCTION

D
rugs and alcohol are often used in an attempt to cope with difficult emotions, and people can quickly become addicted because of the way the brain responds. Addictions carry a whole new set of challenges, often leaving the drug addict stuck in a cycle of substance addiction, struggling to escape and relapse.

Many of us are battling addictions, according to the NHS, hospital admissions with a diagnosis of drug-related mental health and behavioral problems rose by 6 percent in 2015/16. This is higher than in 2005/06 by 11 percent.

It can be extremely hard to control addiction, affecting all aspects of your life, including employment, relationships, and mental and physical health. In this book, we will take a closer look at addiction and discuss how opioid abuse hypnotherapy can be a part of your recovery.

In most cases, the substances activate the reward system of the brain, releasing dopamine, the feel-good hormone. The reward system controls the ability of the body to feel pleasure, and so when triggered, it encourages you to retrigger it. The reward system is over-stimulated when drugs are involved, leading to a 'high.' That high makes people want to take the drug over and over again.

Over time, the brain learns to generate less dopamine and/or make the cells less sensitive to the reward system. It means to the user, the medication does not have the same effect and will create a tolerance. It causes them to want to get high again on more of the drug.

The absence of dopamine can also make it difficult for the affected person to enjoy certain things, such as seeing friends, enjoying a nice meal, or having hobbies.

If the drug is taken on a long-term basis, it can lead to further changes in the chemistry of the brain, affecting memory, decision-making skills, judgment, ability to learn, and tolerance to stress. The mental well-being can also be affected depending on which drug is being used.

It can cause users to experience different symptoms such as paranoia, anger, anxiety, lack of energy, and even hallucinations.

CHAPTER 2

THE DIFFERENCE BETWEEN DRUG ADDICTION AND DRUG ABUSE

Abuse vs Addiction

Abuse of substances and addiction may seem to be the same, but they are two different concepts: people who abuse drugs may not become addicted to them. By definition, substance abuse is more related to the way people use drugs or alcohol. They misuse them, in an abusive manner, but the effects of such use may not have a significant impact on the other parts of their lives.

However, addiction entails the detrimental physical and psychological consequences brought on by the ongoing misuse of the drug. When people are addicted, it is almost impossible for them to avoid using narcotics or alcohol, unlike those who, for example, take part in binge drinking or misuse of drugs on occasions.

Many people may use drugs or alcohol to alleviate stress or even physical symptoms and for pleasure. If a person takes illegal substances or takes a prescription medication beyond the prescribed guidelines, it is considered substance abuse. Repeated drug abuse may begin to alter parts of the brain, especially the reward center. As a result, people are dependent and are frequently unable to avoid using narcotics or alcohol even though they have experienced adverse consequences, such as a medical emergency, health complications, relationship issues, work difficulties, or legal problems.

In certain cases of substance abuse, individuals may undergo periods during which they abstain completely from drugs and alcohol, followed by periods of heavy use.

The primary distinction between drug abuse and addiction is that substance abuse is a damaging behavior; however, there is still an element of choice. When there is an addiction, the patient does not consciously seek to misuse the drugs. When someone is addicted to a substance, physical dependence on the substance is generally present; however, without being addicted to it, one can be physically dependent on a substance (as people may be taking certain prescription medications as per doctor's instructions).

The Harm of Drug Addiction

However, this is not to say substance abuse is not harmful. Often when people use drugs or alcohol regularly, they can experience adverse consequences. The risk of overdose and the possibility of developing an infectious disease, such as Hepatitis B or C and HIV / AIDS, remain.

Those that are not addicted have general power over their use of the drug. If these people want to avoid using drugs or alcohol, they will usually do so without needing to undergo intensive therapy. However, there is always a chance that this casual use can turn into an addiction, and often that addiction can develop rapidly.

The National Institute on Drug Use and Alcoholism reports that 40 percent of people who start drinking before they are 15 years old will become alcohol dependent.

When Addiction Takes Hold

When a person is addicted, there's no longer the choice to just avoid using drugs or alcohol. But if people want to quit, they won't be able to because of the chemical imbalances and physical dependency that developed. They can also undergo a stage of denial, where they cannot accept that their use of drugs or alcohol is the source of many life problems. In this case, an intervention may be needed to allow people to acknowledge the addiction that causes harm in their lives

What are the Differences between Alcohol and Drugs?

The National Institute of Drug Abuse (NIH) briefly answers this question by placing alcohol, alphabetically, at the top of its published list of "Drugs of Abuse" and the National Alcohol and Drug Dependency Council (NCADD) agrees.

Nonetheless, we have separated alcohol from other substances in our society, generally referring to "alcohol and drugs," granting special status to "alcohol," and, before we forget, alcohol is legal, while most other drugs are not.

Is there any difference between being addicted to alcohol and being addicted to any other kind of drug? Sure, however, both addictions have more in common at the end of a long day than separates them from each other.

Difference between Drug Addictions and Drinking?

Under the subheading above, the term "drugs" does a great deal of work, relating to alcohol, painkillers, cocaine, heroin, benzodiazepines, stimulants, inhalants, and sleeping pills. Not all drugs are equal: users of heroin have described being high as "hidden in a warm blanket where worries are gone," while users of cocaine describe euphoria, elevated self-confidence, and a desire to be with others.

But irrespective of the characteristics that differentiate drugs from each other, we define two categories for our immediate purposes: alcohol and other substances.

How Legality Impacts Addiction

Since 1933, when prohibition was repealed, Americans of the prescribed age in their state were able to legally purchase alcohol, and historically, being addicted to a legal drug is more acceptable than being addicted to an illegal one. We joke about too many margaritas; we're not joking about deciding to roll up our sleeve and inject heroin.

It is our cultural attitude towards alcohol, and its legal availability which has probably contributed to the fact that more

Americans are addicted to alcohol than any other drug, more than 18 million of us are addicted to alcohol, with 4.2 million of us addicted to our next most popular drug, marijuana.

So being addicted to a controlled drug can feel different from being addicted to an illicit one.

Stigmas Associated with Drugs and Alcohol

The social stigma attached to addiction appears to be greater when the substance to which one is addicted is illegal: for example, it has been reported that most people working in the healthcare sector have negative perceptions of people using illicit substances, which inevitably influences the services they provide.

The stigma about illicit drug use can also affect one's sense of worth, especially if we consider that a predisposition to low self-esteem is leading to alcohol and drug abuse, taking illicit drugs, and being branded by society as "less," can easily exacerbate an existing issue.

The Difference between Physical Addiction and Alcohol

We may point out certain similarities in how the addiction affects our physical body as we consider illicit drugs as a general category and compare this category to alcohol.

Depression, high blood pressure, ulcers, alcoholic hepatitis, heart damage, liver, pancreas, immune system, comas, strokes, and certain cancers are the most serious effects of alcohol abuse, in terms of its physical effects on our bodies.

Again, in terms of its physical effects on our bodies, the more serious effects of drug abuse are overdose, violent or accidental death, organ failure due to accumulated toxicity, and getting a disease, such as HIV, while addicted.

Although the physical effects left by alcohol and drugs are different, we must understand addiction in terms of its total human cost.

The Independent Scientific Committee on Drugs rates drugs, including alcohol, by the level of harm they do to us, and alcohol rates as the most dangerous substance, at 72 on their scale, while ecstasy rates a 9, for instance. But it is their similarities that the addicted person feels most closely, and not their differences, whether it's a painkiller or vodka that soothes their inner turmoil.

The Impacts of Drug and Alcohol Abuse

Addictive substances can fundamentally change our lives: they can cause us to be cruel to the people we love, to lose our job, to spend money we don't have, to harm our physical bodies, and more. Addiction is less about what drug you are worried about than why you want it.

Many experts will disagree with the similarities and differences between addictions to drugs and alcohol because both are forms of addiction.

How Drug and Alcohol Abuse Differ

Alcoholism is a concept that refers to alcohol addiction, while drug addiction is a generic disorder in which one can be addicted to any substance.

Drugs are addictive substances that change how the body handles information and processes communication.

How are Addictions to Drugs and Alcohol Similar

The symptoms of alcoholism and drug dependence are similar and can be treated using the same techniques. Alcohol addiction is simply a subset of the broader category of drug addiction.

Although not all addictions cause the same feelings or symptoms of withdrawal, all substance abuse originates from similar sources, such as the desire to numb physical or emotional pain.

THE IMPORTANCE OF TREATING DRUG ADDICTION

The only way to rescue your life from the chaos of drug abuse is to join a substance abuse recovery program; approximately 28 million people around the globe battled a substance use disorder in 2016. But only a small percentage, 10 percent get the counseling they need.

There are a host of explanations of why people put off therapy. Many feel ashamed to admit needing help because of the social stigma surrounding addiction. Some do not want to leave their jobs, families, or other commitments.

While having issues is entirely understandable, if left

unaddressed, an addiction can escalate over time. Avoiding therapy can have long-term consequences.

- Damages to romantic and family relationships.

- Economic issues resulting from money spent on drug use.

- Mental and physical health degradation.

- Legal problems, such as charged for unlawful possession.

- Career loss.

The most frightening thing you've ever done could be facing your addiction head-on. Yet you needn't do it by yourself. The care counselors will take you through the entire process of rehabilitation, and tell you what to expect.

The services are as much in your hands, as people in recovery themselves and can relate to what you're going through. We will help find the best recovery facility for you, as well as plans for medical services and post-rehabilitation care. Halfway houses, community groups, and one-on-one counseling provide aftercare options.

CHAPTER 3

STATISTICS ON ADDICTION IN THE WORLD

W hether it's an alcohol, opioid, cocaine, or some other drug, addiction kills thousands of Americans each year and affects millions of lives. Addiction is a psychiatric illness that compels someone to use drugs regularly or participate in habits even though they have negative consequences. Addictions disrupt relationships, friendships, and work, and endanger the basic health and safety of an individual.

- About 21 million Americans have at least one problem, but just 10 percent are treated.

- Death from opioid poisoning has more than tripled since 1990.

- More than 700,000 Americans died from opioid overdoses from 1999 to 2017.

- Alcohol and drug dependence cost the US economy more than $600 billion a year.

- In 2017 34.2 million Americans committed DUI, 21.4 million under alcohol control, and 12.8 million under opioid control.

- Nearly 20 percent of Americans with depression or anxiety disorder still have a drug use disorder.

- More than 90 percent of addicted people started drinking alcohol or consuming drugs before they turned 18.

- Americans aged 18 to 25 are more likely to take addictive medications.

- Alcohol Addiction and Abuse Statistics

Alcohol is the most abused drug in the U.S., and alcoholism is still left untreated. Addiction to alcohol is harmful to the physical, emotional, and social health of an individual.

- Alcohol is the source of 5.3 percent of deaths globally per year (or 1 in 20).

- Around 300 million people worldwide suffer from alcohol use disorder.

- On average, 30 Americans die in an alcohol-related car accident every day, and six Americans die from alcohol poisoning every day.

- Approximately 88,000 people in the United States die each year from alcohol.

- Nearly 6 percent of American adults (about 15 million people) suffer from alcohol use disorder, but only about 7 percent of Americans addicted to alcohol are medically treated.

- Men aged 18 to 25 are more likely to binge drink and become alcoholics.

- Roughly 2,3 million Americans between the ages of 12 and 17 and 2,4 million Americans between the ages of 18 and 25 began drinking alcohol in 2017.

- A relatively low number of high school students in the USA reported consuming alcohol in 2018. Only 18% of 10th graders and 30% of 12th graders admitted to drinking underage in 2018 compared with 25% of 10th graders and 39% of 12th graders in 2013.

Statistics on Opioid Addiction and Abuse

Opioids are a class of medications that block pain sensations and cause euphoria. These are risky because these pose very high addiction and overdose risks. Opioids are a component of many drugs that alleviate pain. Since they are controlled drugs, they are also illegally marketed by drug dealers. Opioids, both illegal and prescribed, in the last two decades have caused a surge in deaths in the United States.

- Nearly 130 Americans die from opioid overdose each day.

- 399,230 Americans lost their lives to opioids from 1999 until 2017.

- In 2017 alone, 47,600 fatal overdoses included at least one opioid in the United States.

- Physicians issued 191,218,272 opioid prescriptions in 2017, a small decrease from the 200,000,000 opioid prescriptions they issued each year between 2006 and 2016.

- Sales of prescription painkillers have increased by 300 percent since 1999.

- Nearly 20 to 30 percent of people taking prescription drugs are misusing them.

- For the first time in 2017, 2 million Americans misused prescription drugs.

- Nearly 10 percent of people who abuse prescription drugs are opioid-addicted.

- About 2.1 million Americans suffer from opioid use disorder.

- Nearly 5 percent of people suffering from opioid use disorder will try heroin.

Heroin addiction and abuse statistics

Heroin is a potent drug and is also highly addictive. It is an illegal drug that poses significant risks of overdose. Heroin, particularly heroin mixed with fentanyl, has been an important contributor to the U.S. opioid epidemic.

- Nearly 494,000 Americans older than 12 are daily users of heroin.

- In 2017 886,000 Americans used heroin at least once.

- Approximately 25 percent of people trying heroin will become addicted.

- In 2017, there were 81,000 Americans who used heroin for the first time.

- In 2017 more than 15,000 Americans died of a heroin overdose.

Marijuana Abuse and Addiction Statistics

Marijuana is a psychoactive substance that originates from a cannabis plant that contains THC. It's becoming increasingly legal in the United States for both medicine and entertainment, but it's still not completely healthy because it can be addictive and trigger health problems.

- Every year roughly 30-40 million Americans smoke marijuana.

- Nearly 43 percent of American adults confess to having tried marijuana.

- In 2017, for the first time, 12 million Americans aged 12 to 17 and 525,000 Americans aged 26 years and over, used marijuana.

- In 2018, 13% of 8th graders, 27% of 10th graders, and 35% of 12th graders had used marijuana at least once in the previous year. Less than 1 percent of 8th graders reported using it every day, about 3 percent of 10th graders, and about 5 percent of 12th graders.

- Nearly 30 percent of people who use marijuana regularly show drug use disorder.

- The average marijuana batch in 1990 contained less than 4% THC but has since risen to more than 12%. The average marijuana batch has become more potent.

Tobacco-Addiction and Abuse Statistics

In most states, anyone over 18 can buy a packet of cigarettes with ease. While cigarettes are legal and affordable, they trigger several fatal health conditions and are addictive as well.

- Approximately 34 million Americans smoke cigarettes.

- The percentage of Americans smoking cigarettes went down from 21% in 2005 to 14% in 2017.

- About 16 percent of American men smoke cigarettes and about 12 percent of American women.

- People with disabilities are more likely to smoke cigarettes, live below the poverty line, or lack a college education.

- In 2017 about 604,000 Americans aged 12 to 17 and about 1.2 million Americans aged 18 to 21 smoked their first cigarette.

- Tobacco smoking was the source of more than 480,000 deaths in the United States last year.

Cocaine Use and Addiction Abuse

Cocaine is an unlawful stimulant. Either in the form of powder or crystal (commonly referred to as "crack"), cocaine can damage organs, cause mental problems, and cause respiratory failure. Also, cocaine is very addictive. Some users of cocaine may become addicted after only one use of the drug.

- Close to 5 million Americans regularly use cocaine.

- In 2017, at least once in the previous month, 2.2 million Americans used cocaine.

- In 2017, cocaine was involved in 1 in 5 overdose deaths.

- The number of deaths associated with cocaine overdose rose by 34 percent between 2016 and 2017.

- Americans aged 18 and 25 are more likely to use cocaine than any other age group.

- In 2017, for the first time, 1 million Americans over 12 years old used cocaine.

- Almost 4 percent of 12th graders admitted using cocaine at least once in their lives in 2018.

Methamphetamine Abuse and Addiction Abuse

Methamphetamine, widely known as meth, is a controlled drug that has significant potential for misuse, overdose, and addiction. As an illegal drug, meth is usually sold to be burned and smoked as "crystal" (white rocks or fragments). Meth is highly addictive and endangering to the health of an individual.

- The daily Meth consumers are around 774,000 Americans.

Approximately 16,000 of these are aged 12 to 17.

- In 2017 some 10,000 Americans who used meth daily experienced a fatal overdose.

- About 964,000 Americans have meth addictions.

- The first time 195,000 Americans using meth was in 2017.

- Deaths from meth almost tripled between 2011 and 2016.

Statistics on Hallucinogenic Abuse and Addiction

Hallucinogens are a class of drugs that alter the mind. Hallucinogenic drugs include psilocybin mushrooms, DMT, mescaline, LSD, PCP, ketamine, ecstasy, and salvia. All of them are illegal, and all carry risks of dangerous hallucinations, impaired judgment, and addiction.

- In the United States, about 1.4 million people are regular users of hallucinogenic substances. Of these, about 143,000 are minors between the ages of 12 and 17.

- In 2017, 1.2 million Americans used hallucinogens for the first time, including 344,000 minors between the ages of 12 and 17.

- In 2018, 2 percent of 12th graders admitted to hallucinogen use at least once in their lifetime.

Inhalant Addiction and Abuse Statistics

Inhalants are a group of solvents, gases, and sprays from aerosols that people inhale to get high. Inhalants are household items such as nail polish, paint, hair spray, and leather cleaner, but they have effects that change the mind. Using inhalants, called "huffing" can cause a person to lose consciousness or develop an addiction.

- More than 23 million Americans have used inhalants at least once in their lives.

- Some 556,000 Americans are regular users of inhalants.

- Almost 9 percent of 12th graders reported using an inhalant in 2018.

- Inhalants cause nearly 15 percent of suffocation deaths per year.

Get Addiction Help Today

To be an addict to anything is a serious issue. If you leave addiction untreated, your life might be stopped in its tracks. Luckily, across the country, there are many rehabilitation services and recovery centers where anyone can get the care they need to control their addiction.

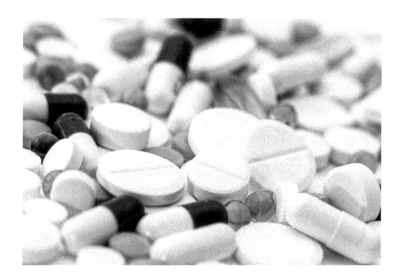

CHAPTER 4

THE FACTORS CONTRIBUTING TO DRUG ADDICTION

What Factors Contribute to Drug Addiction?

D o you ever wonder why you got hooked, and your siblings do not? Substance abuse is rather individualistic, various causes overlap, and they all have essential roles to play. The main contributors to the creation of dependency include:

1. Genetics

While some claim that the origins of addiction lie on the cellular level, deep inside you, there are as many variables as our individual DNA. This is why brothers and sisters frequently take very different routes, some leading to abuse and others not. Nevertheless, genetics do play a part in predisposing you to develop an addiction.

Genes are significant also, according to the American Psychological Association-genetic factors contribute to about half the likelihood of a person becoming addicted. Our genes could lead to:

- Quicker Drug Response.

- The capacity to feel any negative effects decreased.

- Raising euphoria.

- Rapid involvement in repetitive behaviors that is, an addictive personality.

- Such genetic factors may cause experimental drug use to spin out of control quickly and make stopping difficult.

2. Environment

Studies have shown genetics alone do not make an addict. Like so many others, the home in which you and your siblings grew up often plays an important part in your addiction. Several factors play a role in this:

- Divorce.

- Mental illness.

- Frequent arguments.

- Alcohol and drug abuse.

Maybe your parents remained together but argued fiercely and often. Experts believe the level of stress generated in us by this type of behavior can predispose us to become addicted to killing the pain. They also fear that some children are growing up to emulate drug and alcohol abuse by their parents.

The place where an addict lives also plays a part. If you live in a neighborhood where drug use is commonplace, then you start to see it as normal, and the logic of everyone-is-doing-it comes into play.

Working in that type of setting can also be stressful, which can lead to addiction by numbing the anxiety and worries one may feel.

3. Trauma

Traumatic experiences can leave a scar on the psyche, and victims tend to numb their pain with their medication of choice over time. Such incidents are:

- Verbal abuse.

- Neglect.

- Sexual abuse.

- Physical abuse.

- Natural disasters.

- Physical altercations.

- Accidents.

- Terrorism.

The link behind this sort of childhood trauma and the misuse of adult drugs is shocking. Statistics indicate that one in four American children witnesses at least one of these childhood traumas. Exposure to trauma has also been shown to be correlated with an increased chance of addiction, even after becoming an adult.

4. Mental illness

There is a close connection between mental illness and addiction. More than half of substance abusers also deal with a mental illness, according to the National Alliance on Mental Illness.

Certain addicts, do it to alleviate the discomfort and pain associated with the condition. In some, substance addiction sets in motion a chain of events that trigger a diagnosis of mental illness.

5. Peer Pressure

Although many people primarily equate peer pressure with children and teens, this often presents itself in adults. The influences are usually around who they are living with. A partner may join in and begin to abuse drugs with their spouse in hoping to re-experience that first high. Others interpret this as a way of keeping harmony in their relationship. While it may seem like a solution at the time to replace combat with the use of drugs, it is simply not worth it.

It is important to note that just the way a person responds to things or thinks about them will predispose him or her to becoming addicted to them. For instance, someone who by nature is impulsive makes snap decisions without thinking about the consequences or long-term effects. This impulsiveness throws caution on the wind, and the result is experimenting with all sorts of things, like narcotics or alcohol.

The Health Psychology Journal indicated that aspects of personality such as lack of self-control could be related to having trouble communicating with others, and the use of drugs can help to relieve the discomfort.

These factors have affected the dynamics of your way of life, and make sense of what contributed to your addiction. Nevertheless, it is important to note that none of them is a guaranteed route to drug abuse, which is why addiction is like a storm that seemed to strike one person but not another. In comparison, some people come under this category of causes but have never taken any controlled drugs or have been able to avoid them since their first adverse encounter. Yet some are spinning out of control.

It's essential to remember that anyone who has developed an addiction needs help and hope. You will make the improvements with the right support, which will place you on the road to abstinence.

CHAPTER 5

OVERCOMING DRUG ADDICTION

P repared to handle your drug problem? This step-by-step guide can help you handle the cravings and prevent relapse.

Surmounting Drug Addiction: Decide on a Change

Developing opioid addiction is not a character trait or a sign of weakness and solving the problem takes more than willpower. Abuse of illicit or other prescription medications can cause brain changes, leading to strong cravings and a desire to use that makes abstinence seem like an elusive goal. But recovery is never out of reach, no matter how hopeless your situation appears or how many times you have previously tried and failed. Improvement is achievable, with the right care and assistance.

The first step towards recovery for many people dealing with addiction is realizing that you have a problem, and resolving to make a change. It is natural to feel unsure whether you are ready to continue rehabilitation, or whether you have what it takes. If you're addicted to prescription medicine, you might be concerned about how you'll find an alternative way to treat a medical condition. It's fine feeling uncertain. Committing to abstinence means changing a lot of things, including:

- How you handle stress.

- Whom you allow in your life.

- What you do during your free time.

- The way you think about yourself.

- Taking prescription and over-the-counter medications.

It is also natural to feel guilty about giving up your choice of drug, even though you know it causes problems in your life. Recovery takes time, encouragement, and support, but you can conquer your addiction and regain control of your life by committing to change.

Think About Change

- Keep track of the use of medications and when and how much you use them. That will give you a better understanding of the role that addiction plays in your life.

- List the benefits and drawbacks of stopping and the costs and benefits of continuing the substance use.

- Consider such things as your wife, your children, your pets, your job, or your health. Why do those things affect your substance use?

- Tell someone you're sure about your drug use thoughts.

- Ask yourself if there is something that prevents you from

improving. What can be your support in making the change?

Preparing for Change: 5 Main Steps to Recover from Addiction

1. Know the reasons why you want to improve yourself.

2. Think of the rehabilitation attempts in the past, if any. What went wrong? What didn't happen?

3. Set specific, measurable expectations on your drug use, such as a start date or cap.

4. Block your abuse reminders from your home, office, and other places you visit.

5. Tell family and friends that you are dedicated to the rehabilitation, and ask for their support.

Discover the Ways you can Handle Your Addiction

Once you have committed yourself to recovery, it is time to explore your treatment options. Although addiction treatment may vary depending on the particular drug, a successful program often includes various elements, such as:

Detachment. The first step is generally to rid the body of drugs and control the effects of withdrawal.

Behavioral counseling. Person, group, and/or family counseling can help you discover the root causes of your substance use, restore your relationships, and develop healthy ways to deal with it.

Medication can be used to relieve symptoms of withdrawal,

avoid relapse, or treat any mental health disorder that recurs, such as depression or anxiety.

Long-term follow-up can help prevent recurrence and keep abstinence going. This can include attending frequent in-person support groups or online meetings to help keep track of your recovery.

Residential treatment – Residential treatment includes staying in a facility while receiving intensive treatment and being away from work, education, family, friends, and addiction causes. Residential care will last from a couple of days to several months.

Day treatment / Partial Hospitalization – Partial hospitalization is for people who require regular medical care but who want to stay at home and have a healthy living climate.

Typically, these rehab services run for 7 to 8 hours during the day at a recovery facility, and you return home at night.

Rehabilitation care – These outpatient services can be arranged around the job or school, not a live-in care program. During the day or evening, you are being treated but don't stay overnight. The primary focus is on avoiding relapse.

Safe living arrangements – An intensive care plan, such as residential rehab usually involves living in a safe home. You live in a healthy, caring, and drug-free community, with other recovering addicts. Respite living facilities are helpful if you don't have to go somewhere if you're concerned that going back home too early could lead to a relapse.

THE GUIDE TO FINDING THE RIGHT CARE FOR YOUR ADDICTION

For some people, no therapy works. Everyone has different needs. Whether you have an illegal or prescription drug problem, addiction treatment should be tailored to your unique situation. It's important to find a program that makes you feel good.

Treatment can cover more than just substance addiction. Addiction impacts your entire life, including relationships, employment, health, and well-being. The success of the treatment depends on developing a new way of living and addressing the reasons you first turned to drugs.

For example, your opioid dependency may have developed from a need to cope with pain or stress, in which case you need to find a better way to alleviate pain or deal with stressful circumstances.

Commitment and monitoring are important. Treatment with drug addiction isn't a fast and easy operation. Typically speaking, the longer and more intense the use of medications, the longer and more intensive the care you'll need, and the long-term follow-up treatment is essential for rehabilitation in all cases.

There are plenty of places to turn to for help. Not everybody wants medically supervised detox or a lengthy rehab period. The treatment you need depends on several factors including your age, history of substance use, medical or psychological conditions. Apart from physicians and psychiatrists, members of the church, social workers, and counselors provide recovery programs for addictions.

Drug misuse and mental well-being. When you are seeking help with opioid abuse, it is also necessary to get care for any other medical or psychological issues that you encounter. Your best hope of success is to get mental health and alcohol care combined from the same treatment provider or team.

Seeking Help to Recuperate from Your Addiction

Don't try to go it alone – get help. Whatever treatment strategy you choose, it's important to have positive influences and a strong support network. The chances of recovery are better, the more people you can turn to for encouragement, guidance, and a listening ear.

Depend on family and close friends. Getting the help of family and friends is an important step in recovery. If you are reluctant to turn to your loved ones because you have let them down before, consider going to counseling or family therapy for the relationship.

Build a sober social network. You might need to make some new connections if your previous social life revolved around drugs. Sober friends are valuable to have who will help your recovery. Try to take a class, join a church or a civic group, volunteer, or attend community events.

Try Moving into a Safe Home.

Safe homes offer a secure and compassionate place to stay as you recover from opioid dependency. When you don't have a safe home or a drug-free living atmosphere, they are a good choice.

Enter a support group for treatment, such as a 12-step program, and regularly attend meetings. It can be very helpful to spend time with people who understand just what you're going through. You can also take advantage of the group members' shared experiences and learn what others have done to remain free from substance abuse.

Learn safe ways to handle stress

Since coping with your immediate addiction issues and beginning therapy, you will always face the challenges that contributed to your substance abuse. Have you started reducing intense feelings, soothing yourself after an argument, unwinding after a rough day, or ignoring your problems?

When you're drug-free, the negative emotions you've dampened with drugs are resurfacing. To be effective in therapy, you'll need to address the underlying problems first.

You will sometimes continue to experience stress, loneliness, frustration, anger, shame, anxiety, and hopelessness once you have addressed your underlying issues. These thoughts are a natural part of life. An essential component of your treatment and recovery is finding ways to address these feelings as they arise.

There are safe ways to keep an eye on your stress level. You should learn how to handle your issues without reverting to your addiction. Facing intense emotions isn't as daunting or frustrating when you're comfortable in your ability to easily de-stress.

Rapidly Relieve Pain Without Drugs

In some people, different fast stress reduction techniques perform better than others. The trick is to find the one that suits you best.

Move. A brisk walk around the block can suffice to alleviate stress. Also, yoga and meditation are perfect ways to relieve tension and achieve peace.

Step outside and savor the fresh air and warm sun. Enjoy a stunning view of the surrounding countryside.

Play with a Cat or Dog. Love your Pet's Soothing Presence.

Experiment with the sense of smell. Breathe in the fragrance of fresh flowers or coffee beans or savor a smell that reminds you of a favorite holiday, such as sunscreen or a seashell.

Close your eyes, and imagine a peaceful place. Think of a sandy beach, or a fond memory, like the first steps or time your child has spent with friends.

Pamper yourself. Make yourself a steaming cup of tea, take a rub to your neck or back. Immerse yourself in a hot bath or shower.

Keep an Eye on Alcohol Cravings

The healing does not end with getting yourself sober. Your brain also needs time to heal and repair links that have changed when you become addicted. Drug cravings can be intense during this rebuild. By avoiding people, locations, and situations that cause your urge to drink, you can help your continued recovery.

Move away from those friends who are using. Don't hang out with those people who still take drugs. Surround yourself with people who help your abstinence, not the ones who tempt you to fall back into unhealthy, harmful patterns.

Stay away from clubs and pubs. Even if you don't have an alcohol addiction, drinking can weaken inhibitions and impair judgment which can easily lead to relapse. Drugs are often readily available and give you the desire to use them. Avoid all other conditions and circumstances you associate with drug use as well.

If seeking medical attention, be frank about your history of drug use. If you need to get a medical or dental operation done, be upfront, and find a doctor who can work with you either to administer alternatives or to provide the very minimum required medicine. You should never feel guilty or embarrassed about past use of medications or be refused pain medication; if that happens, you will find another doctor.

Use prescription medications with caution. If you've been addicted to prescription medication, such as an opioid painkiller, you may need to speak to your doctor about finding better ways to treat pain. It's crucial to stay away from prescription drugs with the potential for misuse or use only when required and with extreme caution, regardless of the medication you've had issues with. Medications that have a high potential for misuse include painkillers, sleeping pills, and anti-anxiety drugs.

Tackling Alcohol Cravings

Craving can't be stopped at times and a way to cope needs to be found.

Engage in some distracting activity. Write, see friends, go to a movie, dive into a sport, walk or exercise. When you are involved in something else, you will find that the impulses are gone.

Speak honestly, though. Speak to family or friends about addiction when it happens. Talking can be of great help in identifying the source of the craving. Speaking of craving often also helps discharge and relieve the feeling and helps to restore honesty in your relationship. Craving is nothing about which to feel bad.

Challenge your feelings, and alter them. When experiencing a craving, many people tend to remember only the drug's positive effects and forget about the negative effects. So, you may find it helpful to remember that you're not going to feel better if you're using it and that you're going to lose a lot.

Often, it's nice to have these effects written on a small card you keep with you.

Urge control. By toughening it out, many people try to cope with their urges. But there are certain cravings too strong to ignore. When this happens, sticking with the impulse until it passes can be beneficial. This technique is known as urge surfing. Imagine being a surfer who can ride your drug seeking wave, staying on top of it until it crests, splits, and transforms into weaker, foamy surfing. When you ride out the craving, without attempting to fight, judge, or ignore it, you will see that it passes faster than you would think.

The three basic stages of the urge to surf:

1. Notice how you're feeling the urge. Sit in a comfortable chair with your feet on the floor. With your feet down, and relaxed pose with your hands. Take some deep breaths, and concentrate on your body. Note where you feel the attraction or urge in your body, and how it feels. Verbalize what you feel. You might say to yourself, for example: "My addiction is in my mouth and nose, and my stomach."

2. Reflect on one place where you feel desire. Which sensations do you have in that area? Describe them to yourself. Perhaps you feel hot, cold, tingly, or numb, for example? Maybe you have tight muscles? How big an area is involved? Note if the sensations change when you are focused on them. "My mouth is running dry. My lips are full of numbness. I can imagine the sensation of using when I cough."

3. Repeat by concentrating on every part of your body which

is feeling the urge. Describe how the feelings shift, and how the desire comes and goes. Most people find that their cravings have vanished after a few minutes of surfing. However, the object of this exercise is not to wash away the urge but to experience it in a new way. If you practice urge surfing regularly, you can become more comfortable with your cravings, and find it easier to ride them out before they eventually go away.

CREATING A HEALTHY LIFE WITHOUT DRUGS

You will help your addiction recovery by having hobbies and interests that add meaning to your life and protect yourself from relapse. It's important to be involved in things you enjoy, making you feel good, and adding meaning to your life. The addiction will lose its appeal when life is filled with rewarding experiences and a sense of purpose.

Take an old hobby, or seek something new. Do things that test your curiosity and ignite your imagination, something you've always wanted to try. Study a foreign language, a musical instrument, or try a new sport.

Adopt a pet. Sure, pets are a burden, but you feel loved and need to look after an animal. You can take pets out of the house for exercise as well.

Spend time in the wild. Take a scenic hike, go fishing or camping in a park, or enjoy frequent walks.

Support the arts. Visit a museum, go to a play or concert, take an art class, or write a memoir.

Be a representative of your community. Replace your addiction with communities and events which are drug-free. Volunteer, or join a local club or neighborhood group, become active in your church or faith community.

Set concrete goals. Having goals to work for can be important antidotes to opioid abuse, and give you something to look forward to. It doesn't matter what the milestones are; they're just important to you.

Look after your wellbeing. Regular exercise, proper sleep, and healthy eating habits help maintain your energy levels and reduce stress. The more that you can stay safe and feel good, the easier it is to remain sober.

Do not let a relapse bring you down

Relapse is a common part of the drug dependency recovery process. While relapse is painful and depressing, it can be an opportunity to learn from your mistakes, recognize potential causes, and change the course of your treatment.

What causes a relapse?

Various "triggers" can put you at risk of relapse into old substance use patterns. Although specific causes of relapse vary from one person to another, some common triggers include:

- Emotional negative state (such as tension, depression,

frustration, or trauma).

- Good emotional state (feeling satisfied and feeling even better, like having a nice time with your friends).

- Physical malaise (such as pain or symptoms of withdrawal).

- A strong desire or compulsion to use (cravings).

- Conflict (such as a spousal or partner argument).

- Social pressure (to be in a position where someone else appears to be doing it).

The crucial thing to note is that relapse does not mean failure in the opioid treatment. Don't surrender. Call your mentor, speak to your psychiatrist, attend a meeting, or schedule a doctor's appointment. Look at what caused the relapse, what went wrong, and what you should have done better when you're sober again and out of risk. You may opt to get back on the recovery road and use the experience to reaffirm your dedication.

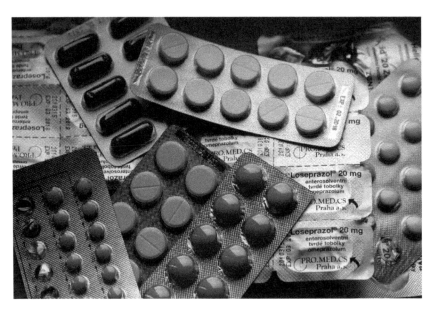

CHAPTER 6

THE EFFECT OF ADDICTION ON THE HUMAN BRAIN

Presenting the Human Brain

The human brain is the most intricate organ in the body. At the center of all human activity is this three-pound mass of grey and white matter, you need it to drive a car, enjoy a meal, breathe, create an artistic masterpiece and enjoy everyday activities. The brain controls the basic functions of your body, helps you to perceive and respond to anything you feel, and forms your behavior. In short, you are your brain — all that you think and feel, and how you are.

How does the Brain Respond?

The brain is usually compared to an incredibly intricate and complex computer. The brain is composed of billions of cells, called neurons, coordinated into circuits and networks rather like electrical circuits on the silicon chips controlling our electronic devices. Each neuron serves as a switch controlling the information flow. If a neuron receives sufficient signals from other neurons to which it is connected, it will fire, transmitting its signal on to other circuit neurons.

The brain consists of several sections of interconnected circuits, all of which function together as a team. Different brain circuits are responsible for coordinating specific functions and performing them. Neuron networks relay messages back and forth to each other, and throughout the rest of the body (the peripheral nervous system) to various parts of the brain, spinal cord, and nerves.

A neuron releases a neurotransmitter to the gap(or synapse) between it and the next cell, to convey a message. The neurotransmitter crosses the synapse and binds the receiving neuron to the receptors, like a key inside a lock. This triggers cell reception modifications. Other molecules, called transporters recycle neurotransmitters (i.e. carry them back into the neuron that produced them), thereby reducing or shutting down the signal between neurons.

Why is it that Drugs Work in the Brain?

Drugs interact with the way neurons use neurotransmitters to send, receive, and interpret signals. Some drugs, including marijuana and heroin, that stimulate neurons because their chemical structure resembles that of a natural neurotransmitter in the body. It allows the drugs to bind themselves to and stimulate the neurons. While these drugs imitate the brain's chemicals, they do not stimulate neurons in the same way as a natural neurotransmitter, and they cause irregular signals to be transmitted across the network.

Certain drugs, such as amphetamine or cocaine, may trigger

abnormally large amounts of natural neurotransmitters to be released by the neurons or interfere with transporters to prevent the regular recycling of these brain chemicals. That too amplifies or disrupts normal neuronal communication.

What Areas of the Brain can a Drug Affect?

Drugs can change significant brain areas required for life-sustaining functions and cause the compulsive use of drugs that defines addiction. Areas of the brain affected by drug use include:

Basal ganglia, which play a significant role in positive types of motivation, including the pleasurable effects of healthy behaviors such as feeding, socializing, and sex, as well as routine development. Both areas form a central node in what is often referred to as the "reward circuit" for the brain. Drugs over-activate this circuit, causing high drug euphoria. Yet with prolonged exposure, the circuit adapts to the drug's presence, diminishing its sensitivity and making it impossible to experience satisfaction from something other than the drug.

- The extended amygdala plays a role in stressful feelings such as anxiety, irritability, and discomfort that characterize withdrawal after the medication is fading and therefore motivates the individual to try the medication again. With increased drug usage, this circuit is ever more responsive. A person with substance use disorder uses medications overtime to get temporary relief from this pain, rather than going high.

- The prefrontal cortex is capable of thought, organizing, solving problems, determining, and exercising self-control over impulses. It is also the last section of the brain to mature, which makes adolescents more vulnerable. Shifting equilibrium between this circuit and the basal ganglia circuits and expanded amygdala makes an individual with a substance use disorder compulsively pursue the drug with decreased impulse control.

Many medications such as opioids often affect certain areas of the brain, such as the brain stem, which regulates essential life-critical basic functions including heart rate, breathing, and sleep. This intervention explains why overdoses can cause death and depressed breathing.

How is it that drugs offer pleasure? Simple daily tasks can create small bursts of neurotransmitters in the brain, bringing pleasurable sensations. Drugs may have stopped this.

Pleasure or euphoria — the high from drugs — is still poorly understood, but presumably includes surges of chemical signaling substances, including natural opioids (endorphins) in the body and other neurotransmitters in parts of the basal ganglia (the reward circuit). When certain medications are taken, these neurotransmitters can cause pulses far greater than the smaller bursts that are normally created in conjunction with healthy rewards such as eating, hearing, or playing music, artistic activities, or social interaction.

It was once believed that drug-induced spikes of the neurotransmitter dopamine directly triggered the euphoria. Scientists now suggest that dopamine has more to do with getting us to repeat pleasurable experiences (reinforcement) than actually creating pleasure.

Why does Dopamine Make Drug use Stronger?

The enjoyment feeling is how a balanced brain recognizes and enhances beneficial habits such as feeding, socializing, and sex. Our minds are designed to increase the likelihood that we will be doing pleasurable things again. Key to this is the neurotransmitter dopamine. Whenever the reward circuit is triggered by a safe, pleasurable feeling, a blast of dopamine shows that something important that needs to be remembered is happening. This dopamine signal induces improvements in neural communication that make it easier to replicate the task without thinking about it, again and again, contributing to habit-forming.

Just as drugs cause extreme euphoria, they also generate much greater bursts of dopamine, strengthening the link between drug use, the accompanying pleasure, and all the visible signs associated with the experience. Massive surges of dopamine "teach" the brain to look for medication at the expense of other healthier goals and activities. Cues in the daily routine or environment of a person that has become associated with drug use due to changes in the reward circuit can trigger uncontrollable cravings whenever the person is exposed to these situations, even if the drug itself is not available. This learned "reflex" can last a long time, even in people who didn't use drugs for many years.

Individuals who have been drug-free for a decade, for instance, may feel cravings when they return to an old neighborhood or house where they used drugs. The brain remembers, like riding a bicycle.

How are Drugs Different?

The difference between natural rewards and drug incentives for the brain can be contrasted with the difference between someone whispering in your ear and someone yelling in a microphone, much like we switch down the volume on a radio that is too noisy, by generating fewer neurotransmitters in the reward system, or through the number of receptors that can interpret signals, the brain of someone who misuses drugs changes. Consequently, the ability of the individual to derive gratification from naturally satisfying (i.e., strengthening) behaviors is also reduced.

This is why a person who misuses drugs ultimately feels lethargic, unmotivated, helpless, and/or depressed and is unable to enjoy previously pleasurable things. Now, to achieve just a small amount of reward, the person has to keep taking drugs — which just makes the issue worse, like a vicious cycle. The individual will also often have to take greater quantities of the drug to achieve the familiar high — an effect is known as tolerance.

CHAPTER 7

UNDERSTANDING ADDICTION

New Insights into Addiction Causes

Addiction requires an intense desire for something, a lack of control over its use, and continuing engagement with it despite adverse effects. Addiction transforms the brain, first by subverting the way gratification is perceived and then by corrupting other natural drives such as learning and motivation. While it is difficult to break an addiction, it can be done.

What Induces Addiction?

The word "addiction" comes from a Latin term for "slaved by" or "bound to." Someone who has tried to overcome an addiction — or sought to help someone else do so — understands why.

Addiction exerts a long and strong impact on the brain, which occurs in three distinct ways: compulsion for the object of addiction, lack of control over its use, and persistent engagement with it despite adverse effects.

Experts have assumed for many years that only alcohol and strong drugs can induce addiction.

Nevertheless, neuroimaging techniques and more recent studies have shown that certain pleasurable behaviors, such as gambling, shopping, and sex, can co-opt the brain too.

Although a standard U.S. diagnostic manual (the Mental Disorders Diagnostic and Statistical Manual, Fourth Edition, or DSM-IV) identifies multiple addictions, each connected to a particular drug or behavior, there is a consensus that these reflect multiple manifestations of a similar underlying brain function.

Fresh Perspectives on a Growing Question

These are the latest figures from the Government:

- Up to 23 million Americans — nearly one in ten — are addicted to alcohol or other substances.

- More than two-thirds of addicted people have substance abuse.

- Hemp, opioid (narcotic) pain relievers and cocaine are the top three substances that cause addiction;

Once psychologists first began studying what triggered addictive behavior in the 1930s, they claimed that people who developed addictions were either psychologically deficient or lacking in willpower. We believed that overcoming addiction required punishing miscreants or, in exchange, inspiring them to muster the courage to break a habit.

Since then, the scientific consensus has shifted. Today we understand addiction as a chronic disease that affects both the structure and function of the brain. Much as cardiovascular disease affects the heart, the pancreas is weakened by diabetes, so alcohol hijacks the brain.

It occurs as the brain undergoes a series of changes, starting with pleasure perception and culminating with a drive toward compulsive behavior.

Pleasure Principle

The brain records all rewards, whether they come from a psychoactive substance, a monetary reward, a sexual experience, or a fulfilling meal. Pleasure has a distinct signature in the brain: the release of the neurotransmitter dopamine in the accumbens nucleus, a cluster of nerve cells located under the cerebral cortex (see illustration). Dopamine release is strongly linked to pleasure in the nucleus accumbens and neuroscientists refer to the area as the center of pleasure for the brain.

All abuse drugs, from nicotine to heroin, cause the nucleus accumbens to have a particularly potent surge of dopamine. The probability that the use of a drug or involvement in a rewarding behavior may result in addiction is directly linked to the speed at which it induces the release of dopamine, the duration of that release, and the durability of that release.

Even taking the same drug through different delivery methods can influence how likely it is to lead to addiction. Smoking or injecting a medication intravenously, as compared, for example, to swallowing it as a tablet, usually produces a quicker, stronger dopamine signal which is more likely to result in substance abuse.

50

The Reward System for the Brain

Addictive drugs provide a gateway to the reward system in the brain by pouring dopamine into the nucleus accumbens. The hippocampus establishes memories of the rapid sense of pleasure, and the amygdala produces a conditioned reaction to certain stimuli.

Learning Process

Researchers once claimed that the feeling of gratification alone was sufficient to motivate people to continue to look for an addictive drug or behavior. Recent analysis, however, indicates that the situation is more complicated. Not only does dopamine contribute to the pleasure experience, but it also plays a role in learning and memory — two key elements in the transition from liking something to becoming addicted to it.

Dopamine combines with another neurotransmitter, glutamate, to take over the reward-related learning system in the brain according to existing addiction theory.

This system plays an important role in sustaining life as it links with enjoyment and reward behaviors required for human survival (such as eating and sex).

The brain reward system involves areas that include both motivation and memory, as well as enjoyment. The same circuit activates addictive drugs and behaviors — and then overloads it.

Repeated exposure to an addictive drug or activity causes the nerve cells in the nucleus accumbens and the prefrontal cortex (the region of the brain involved in planning and performing tasks) to interact in such a way that pairs with wanting it, in effect lead us to obey it. That is, this cycle motivates us to search out the source of gratification and take action.

Why Have you Become Addicted?

It's not entirely easy to determine if you have an addiction. Acknowledging it is not easy, primarily because of the addiction-related stigma and shame. Recognizing the problem, however, is the first step towards recovery.

A "yes" response to any of the following three questions suggests you might have an addiction problem and should, at the very least, meet with a health care professional for further assessment and guidance.

- Do you use more of the drug, or want more often than in the past?

- Do you have signs of withdrawal when you don't have the drug?

- Have you ever lied to anyone about the drug you use or the nature of your behavior?

Developing Tolerance

The brain adapts over time in a way that makes the desired material or action less pleasurable.

Rewards typically come only with time and effort. Addictive

drugs and habits offer a solution, allowing dopamine and other neurotransmitters to enter the brain. Our brains aren't able to handle the onslaught easily.

For example, addictive drugs can release two to ten times the amount of dopamine that natural rewards produce, and they do so faster and more consistently. Brain receptors in a person being addicted get overwhelmed. By generating less dopamine or suppressing dopamine receptors, the brain responds, an adaptation equivalent to turning the volume down on a loudspeaker when noise is too loud.

Dopamine has less effect on the reward core of the brain as a result of such adaptations. Those who develop an addiction usually find that the desired drug doesn't give them as much satisfaction over time.

They will take more of it to get the same "normal" dopamine as their brains have adapted to, an effect known as tolerance.

Compulsion Does Take Over

Compulsion takes over at this stage. The gratification associated with an addictive drug or action subsides — and yet the perception of the desired effect continues, and the need to replicate it. It's as if the usual motivational mechanism is no longer functioning.

Also, the cycle of learning mentioned earlier comes into play. The hippocampus and the amygdala store information regarding environmental signals associated with the desired substance, so that it can be re-located. Such memories help to build a conditioned response — intense desire — whenever the person experiences certain environmental indicators.

For example, a person who is addicted to heroin may run the risk of relapse when he sees a hypodermic needle. In contrast, another person may start drinking again after seeing a bottle of whiskey.

Conditioned learning helps explain why even after years of abstinence, people who develop an addiction risk relapses.

Possible Recovery

As the slogan of the 1980s suggested, "just say no" is not enough. Instead, saying "yes" to other things can protect (and heal) yourself from addiction. Cultivate diverse interests that make your life meaningful. Understand that the problems are typically fleeting, and accept, perhaps most significantly, that life is not always meant to be pleasurable.

Drug addiction has detrimental effects on the mind, actions, and relationships. Still, the chronic effects of drugs on the body will gradually kill vital structures and functions, resulting in permanent impairment or even death. Also, legal drugs, taken to excess, may cause serious effects that cannot be easily undone.

CHAPTER 8

THE LONG-TERM EFFECT OF DRUG ADDICTION

Usage of Cocaine and the Body

W hat cocaine does to both body and mind is well known as one of the most dangerous substances in the world. There are several variables, however, which may affect the long-term physical effects cocaine has on a person.

Drug addiction has detrimental effects on the mind, actions, and relationships. Still, the chronic effects of drugs on the body will gradually kill vital structures and functions, resulting in permanent impairment or even death. Also, legal drugs, taken to excess, may cause serious effects that cannot be easily undone; and excessive use may not even be sufficient for permanent harm to occur with certain illicit drugs.

- Timespan (length of cocaine consumption).

- Consumption frequency.

- What type of cocaine (cocaine hydrochloride versus the "crack" form of the freebase)?

- How the drug was taken (whether snorted, smoked or injected into a vein, because smoking cocaine makes the drug enter the brain faster than snorting, giving immediate effect to the users).

- Average cocaine intake per dose.

- Human genetics, psychology, and physiology, including current mental health status, family background, age, gender, diet, other drug involvement, etc.

Long-term (and probably permanent) effects of cocaine include a reduction in bone density and muscle mass which can contribute to osteoporosis. Cocaine suppresses appetite, so much so that it can be a source and a result of eating disorders. The drug significantly changes the metabolism of the body, making fatty foods useless, and giving addicts far less body fat than those who don't use cocaine.

Profound Metabolic Modification

Food and liquid consumption can also be altered by cocaine, resulting in irreversible changes in body weight (or a "profound metabolic modification," in the words of the Appetite Journal) regardless of diet.

Due to the extensive harm that the drug does to the respiratory system, cocaine misuse can often produce a chronic cough in users; specifically, problems in the upper respiratory and pulmonary systems frequently result in breathing difficulties, leading to inadequate blood flow to the heart muscles (a condition known as ischemia). Repeated exposure to cocaine through snorting and smoking can also cause infections and death of the nasal lining and sinus tissue.

Users may experience chronic cough, chest pain, and fatigue from lung damage (pulmonary edema), as well as pulmonary hemorrhage (lung bleeding) and a variety of other disorders, such as pulmonary barotrauma, foreign body granulomas, cocaine-related pulmonary infection, obliterative bronchiolitis, and asthma, to name a few, reported in the Journal Recent Developments in Alcoholism. Long-term users of cocaine frequently get easily tired, have difficulty breathing, and feel chest pain regularly.

A lot of work has been carried out on what drug addiction does in the long term to the heart and cardiovascular systems. The American Heart Association noted that users of cocaine had "abnormal" blood flow into the vessels of the heart, which can cause serious heart problems or even death. Unfortunately, much of this damage cannot be detected immediately, so users may consume cocaine for prolonged periods before they feel something significantly wrong.

Because of the drug addiction, the arteries of the heart are over dilated, which makes them pump blood much faster than normal, causing the chest pain and shortness of breath. Cocaine also raises blood pressure because the heart has to function harder. The walls of the blood vessels grow weaker over time, and the heart muscle itself can be weakened by the overwork, leading to aneurysms, heart attacks, and death.

Losing Heart and Brain

The Circulation Journal reports other long-term effects of cocaine dependence on the heart and cardiovascular systems, such as myocardial infarction, cardiomyopathy, endocarditis, and aortic dissection. Using cocaine for some time can also worsen pre-existing heart issues, hasten cardiac failure, and cause permanent breathing, digestion, and blood pressure problems.

The harm done to the brain by cocaine will last the longest. Cambridge University research has found that cocaine can make brain age unnaturally fast; addicted users "lose twice the volume of the brain each year" compared to their non-using counterparts. As part of the normal aging process, the brain loses grey matter which manifests as the usual signs of old age such as memory problems and declining cognitive abilities.

Yet middle-aged people who are physically and mentally dependent on cocaine have the same symptoms. The Neuropsychopharmacology report found that some of the damage could be repaired. Still, regeneration of the working memory was only expected during the first year of the termination of "moderate" cocaine use. The assumption is that long-term exposure to cocaine may result in a permanent cognitive deterioration among users, without some form of medical intervention.

Scientists at the University of Michigan School of Medicine found that the drug could permanently kill brain cells, in addition to rapidly aging the brain. Cocaine's ability to improve the output of dopamine in the brain is what gives it the "high" attribute. Researchers also noted that the particular neurons that associate with cocaine use are "damaged and even killed in the drug-use phase."

It acts as a double-edged sword, as trying to discontinue the use of cocaine leads to painful and distressing symptoms of withdrawal, as the brain scrambles to control its processes and function without cocaine. Without proper care and management, this may induce an abuser not only to restart cocaine use but also to raise it in a desperate effort to alleviate the effects of withdrawal and regain the initial feeling of euphoria.

It helps to intensify the death of the neurons and the irreversible damage that occurs to the brain; because the neurons are responsible for causing pleasure feelings and finding rewards, the damage they undergo means that users are unable to receive enjoyment and reward from any other source.

The Methamphetamine Damage

Cocaine isn't the only stimulant to inflict irreversible body damage. Methamphetamines are doing a very similar job of killing the neurotransmitters of dopamine in the brain, and prolonged exposure to the substance can render it difficult for a consumer to feel gratification from some other source. The dopamine receptors can recover with time and care, but damage to the prefrontal centers may be life-long. Research indicates damage to muscle control from chronic meth use is similar to people suffering from Parkinson's disease.

The loss of motor coordination is one effect on the body. Changes in brain chemistry can also lead to violent and unpredictable behavior that affects the user's physical self with a grave toll. Methamphetamines often cause a rise in adrenaline levels, in addition to triggering a huge dopamine overload, which makes users feel nervous and highly-strung all the time, depriving them of sleep and relaxation. Users act hyperactively, fixing on a given object or task, then quickly finding another target for their obsession, and so on.

Severe meth ingestion may lead to hallucinations that cause users to harm their bodies; they feel like insects are crawling under their skin, picking and scratching them until they bleed, a disorder known as formication

Skin and Brain Scars

Other long-term, physical effects of meth include blood vessel damage that impedes regular blood flow to all parts of the body. Even minor injuries may get infected and worsen without the ability to repair themselves, and the skin itself is losing much of its healing and defensive properties. Most patients develop tiny sores in their bodies, which can become open and oozing, combined with the formication.

Meth induces, as with other stimulants, bursts of excessive movement like teeth grinding. Together with poor diet and poor hygiene which are symptoms of substance abuse, heavy meth addicts tend to have broken and rotting teeth. Meth dries the salivary glands, destroying the protective buffering of acids in the mouth; any acidic or sugary foods eaten during a meth binge further damage the teeth, causing multiple cavities. Former addicts need intensive dental work and strict dietary monitoring to ensure the health of their teeth and gums during recovery.

Although some of the effects of extreme methamphetamine abuse may be cosmetic and can be reversed, there is far less forgiveness inside the body about what the drug does. Extreme blood vessel damage increases the risk of stroke, which can result in permanent brain damage or death.

Changes in the Body Through Marijuana

Stimulants such as cocaine and meth are notorious for how they blast the brain into producing dopamine. Still, another substance that can affect the brain's neurotransmitter development and function is marijuana. Tetrahydrocannabinol, the effective chemical compound in marijuana, also triggers the release of dopamine which is why marijuana smokers feel good and satisfied with marijuana smoking or edible marijuana consumption.

Excessive, long-term smoking, however, has been shown to result in dopamine deficiencies in key brain areas, leading researchers to theorize that smoking marijuana to the point of addiction can cause brain damage similar in nature to small quantities of cocaine. This damage affects not just the dopamine neurotransmitters but also the brain's grey matter, contributing to cognitive loss.

Scientists warn the earlier pot-smoking starts, the greater the effect of THC on the still-developing brain (the frontal lobe, which controls cognitive and thinking capacity, is not completely developed until the age of 25), and the issues this creates for later life. A Boston neuroscientist found that adolescents and young adults who smoked marijuana were behaving more impulsively than their peers (which is consistent with other research). A follow-up study showed that people who smoked regularly and recreationally struggled with thought and higher mental processes, particularly if those people started their habit early.

Marijuana, too, can cause other types of long-term body damage. The smoke in marijuana consists of several poisonous chemicals, including hydrogen cyanide and ammonia, which can damage the lung's bronchial passages. As with cocaine addicts, chronic pot smokers can suffer from a persistent cough that can damage the lungs and respiratory passages, as well as a struggle with breathing, fatigue, and excess mucus secretion.

Tetrahydrocannabinol can make the heart increase its rhythm by 50 beats per minute, a condition that can last for three hours; this may cause a heart attack and long-lasting heart damage for smokers who are vulnerable to heart failure or have other health problems. The Journal of the American Heart Association warns that if they smoke enough marijuana to send their hearts into a frenzy, even young people with no family history of heart trouble could suffer from heart rhythm problems.

Can Alcohol Cause Permanent Body Damage?

Even alcohol can severely harm the body if abused and is the most common drug of all. Alcohol affects the internal communication networks of the brain, triggering mood and behavior disturbances and making it more difficult to think and to focus. A severe example of this is a disease known as Korsakoff's Syndrome. This brain disorder occurs when long-term consumption of alcohol so dramatically affects the brain's chemical structure that users lose control of their motor function, have trouble walking, and have vision problems.

Korsakoff's Syndrome is caused by thiamine (vitamin B1) deficiency in the brain and central nervous system. The body does not produce thiamine, so it is found in foods such as pork and yeast.

Alcoholics tend to have poor nutrition because their environment is corrupted by addiction, because of the damage to the stomach lining caused by a constant flow of alcohol; this, in turn, causes frequent vomiting which further damages the stomach and empties the body of what little nutrients it has left. The result is that chronic drinkers get inadequate thiamine in their diet. Korsakoff 's Syndrome sets in as the condition worsens. Like cocaine, excessive consumption of alcohol can also harm the heart.

Conditions include alcoholic cardiomyopathy, a type of heart disease in which the organ is slowly weakened and its muscles thinned by excessive intake of alcohol.

This affects the efficiency of blood-pumping processes of the heart, resulting in a lack of supply to major organs and systems of the body. It will, at worst, cause heart failure and a variety of other dangerous conditions. Those who are diagnosed with alcoholic cardiomyopathy (men more than women, but also women) appear to have a long-term history of extreme alcohol use.

The condition does not often cause symptoms; when symptoms arise, they are close to those of heart failures, such as exhaustion, trouble breathing, and swelling of the legs and feet, which is caused by fluid accumulation because the heart cannot adequately pump blood to the extremities. Blood needs to travel through the veins to the heart, allowing fluid to pool in the stomach and lower extremities, causing swelling.

Strokes Which are Caused by Alcohol

Further drug damage to the brain may have permanent effects on the body, including the risk of a stroke caused by alcohol. Research published in the journal Stroke indicated that too much middle-aged alcohol (more than two drinks a day) raises a stroke's risk by 34 percent, the same degree as high blood pressure or diabetes. Those who drink too much in their 50s and 60s have a much higher risk of having strokes than people of the same age who drink lightly or not at all. The lead author of the Stroke report said drinking more than two drinks a day "can shorten the time for stroke by around five years."

Researchers have theorized that the risk of a hemorrhagic stroke (where a blood vessel bursts within the brain) is increasing because alcohol thins the blood—the more alcohol in the blood, the greater the risk that the brain would bleed. For the two forms for strokes that can occur (ischemic and hemorrhagic), hemorrhagic strokes are the most serious; in addition to interrupting blood flow, internal bleeding can often raise cranial pressure, which can physically harm the brain tissue.

Alcohol and Liver Damage

The ongoing effects of substance dependence on the liver are well known. A healthy liver does many things as the second largest organ in the body, including processing food and liquid into energy and nutrients for the rest of the body and filtering out harmful substances in the blood. Too much alcohol can damage the liver cells and even destroy them. The liver easily breaks down alcohol for disposal by the body under normal circumstances; too much alcohol overwhelms the liver, causing a variety of diseases that affect the rest of the body, such as alcoholic fatty liver disease, alcoholic hepatitis, and alcoholic cirrhosis.

Alcoholic fatty liver disease occurs as a result of depositing fat in the hepatic cells. Symptoms are rare, but they manifest as fatigue, weakness, and abdominal pain when they occur. Alcoholic fatty liver disorder may be reversed by deliberately stopping the intake of alcohol under medical supervision.

Alcoholic hepatitis is the product of inflammation and mild liver scarring, often caused by the liver having more alcohol to absorb than it can. Symptoms may include a lack of appetite and vomiting (which leads to the risk of Korsakoff 's Syndrome), as well as nausea, stomach pain, fever, and yellowing. As many as 35 percent of heavy drinkers tend to develop alcoholic hepatitis, which may occur in either moderate or serious ways. With slowly weaning off alcoholic consumption, mild alcoholic hepatitis can be reversed. Still, the extreme form of the disease can start without warning and can lead to emergency complications, such as liver failure and eventually, death.

Finally, alcoholic cirrhosis is described as the most advanced type of injury that can be incurred by the liver due to alcohol abuse.

The scarring and damage of normal liver function are severe; hard scar tissue replaces the soft tissue in a healthy liver. About 10 % to 20% of heavy drinkers experience alcoholic cirrhosis, but those are the people who drink to the most dangerous level. Even abstinence cannot cure cirrhosis, resulting in irreversible damage to the liver; however, abstinence and treatment can avoid further damage, although certain symptoms (similar to those of serious alcoholic hepatitis) can persist for life.

Life-Threatening Effects

If a person who drinks too much develops liver disease associated with alcohol, the progression begins with fatty liver disease, progresses to alcoholic hepatitis, and culminates in alcoholic cirrhosis. But some heavy drinkers may first develop cirrhosis, bypassing the stage of hepatitis. Many drinkers may contract alcoholic hepatitis, but they never show the symptoms. Non-alcoholic liver diseases, like chronic Hepatitis C, can exacerbate liver damage caused by excessive alcohol consumption.

The risk of developing an alcoholic liver disease that may permanently affect the liver depends on a variety of different factors, such as a family history of liver disorders and drug abuse, diet, age, gender, lifestyle, and other medical or mental health conditions that could lead to the development of an alcohol misuse disorder. The risks that occur may be life-threatening. Such risks involve internal bleeding (usually from the stomach or even from the esophagus, which may occur as coughing blood), hyposplenism, kidney failure, and hepatic cancer.

In Scientific American, a professor of neurocognitive development writes that heavy alcohol consumption changes the structure and composition of the brain and the body. After years of abstinence, there is no telling how much can be regained.

Some studies have suggested affected areas of the brain may "return to their original volume and repair neural connections" if abstinence is maintained which would bode well for the physical impact of alcoholism. Some work has, however, found "sustained damage in some places," indicating that even complete recovery may only have minimal effectiveness in body reconstruction after long-term abuse.

CHAPTER 9

HYPNOTHERAPY FOR DRUG ABUSE

Hypnosis or hypnotherapy as a cure for addiction is gaining acceptance within the medical and psychiatric communities. When done under a highly skilled addiction counselor's watchful eye, this therapy will help those who have already gone through the early stages of recovery deal with cravings and stave off relapse.

Process for Hypnotherapy Treating Addiction

During the recovery process, hypnotherapy as a cure for addiction comes later. Before they even consider undergoing treatment, the person seeking treatment needs to completely detoxify their system, and this usually means spending weeks or even months cleaning up.

The hypnotherapist is a medical practitioner who uses hypnosis as a therapy for addictions. The hypnotherapist leads the patient who is recovering into a trance-like mental state in which the addict becomes more open to thoughts and suggestions. Anyone being hypnotized in this state will become more creative and successful at solving the problems. They are in prime place, in short, to figure out tactics to overcome their addictive habits.

The only way hypnosis can be successful as addiction treatment, however, is if the person being hypnotized genuinely wants to give up their addictive habits and behaviors.

The treatment doesn't change minds or create new perspectives. Instead, it helps to hone a pre-existing mentality and refine it.

Hypnosis as a Treatment for Addiction

Understanding that hypnosis is not a cure-all for addiction is important, but it can serve a role in a comprehensive course of treatment. It's particularly useful to help recovering alcoholics remain on the right track.

The person seeking care must be sober for hypnotherapy to play a significant function in overcoming addictions. Deep concentration is the cornerstone of hypnotism, and the toxins and dulling effects of alcohol limit a hypnotic trance's effectiveness.

Hypnosis serves a greater role in preventing relapse, than in quitting drinking. This acts as motivation but not in itself a cure to addiction.

A new set of problems arise when a person who has suffered from an alcohol problem overcomes the initial obstacle of becoming sober. Staying sober at this stage is the objective, and that involves setting goals, plenty of concentration, and a healthy dose of optimism.

It is where hypnosis is successful as a cure for addiction. It helps the patient to become active in the recovery process, helping them to discover their relapse causes and to provide them with resources to deconstruct a relapse should one occur.

Hypnosis Helps to Relax

The hypnotic trance is a deeply relaxed state, marked by changes in the patterns of metabolism, breathing, and even brain. In other words, it is both a state of being, mentally, and physically.

In this relaxed state, the hypnotized person becomes more open to understanding the mechanisms of their alcohol addiction. It helps them to experience the ebb and flow of their cravings to put together strategies to resolve them, without dealing with any tension or feelings of remorse.

Self-Hypnosis

In some cases, the hypnotherapist may also train its patients in their daily lives to practice self-hypnosis. Going into a mildly hypnotic state is an ideal way to resolve an addiction in real-time, and it offers a powerful advantage over relapse to recovering alcoholics.

Specialists in Hypnotism for Addiction

One of the most critical factors when pursuing hypnosis as an addiction therapy is who will be conducting the therapeutic procedure. There are very few rules governing who can and cannot practice hypnotism, which means the best practitioners are worth searching for.

The level of expertise needed by a specialist depends to a

certain extent on the scope of the therapy. A simple behavioral therapy is more than suitable for recovering alcoholics who are attempting to arm themselves with techniques to ward off cravings and relapse.

This level of hypnotism is fairly easy to execute, and while it definitely shouldn't be practiced by amateurs, it can be learned. An association such as the American Society of Clinical Hypnosis will recognize any practitioner who uses hypnosis as a treatment for addictions.

Yet several rehabilitation services and drug recovery facilities often use hypnotherapy as a way to dig into the mind of the client to find out the underlying causes of addictive behavior. This requires thorough knowledge of the addiction psychology, which can only be achieved under the strict supervision of a trained psychologist.

The Hypnosis Limits for Alcohol Treatment

In considering the effectiveness of hypnosis as a treatment for addiction, recognition of the different types of addiction that exist is important. In short, drug addiction can operate on a mental or physical level. In certain instances, there are elements of both.

A physical addiction includes an alcohol-like substance that physically enters the body and changes how it operates. The harm done on the body by the drug can be reversible, but no amount of hypnosis can reverse such physical changes. That's the equivalent to requiring antivirus software to fix computer hardware issues.

Yet from a mental viewpoint, an addiction is embedded in repeated habits, and the reward comes in some sort of pleasure or catharsis. Many addictions are purely behavioral, for example, gambling addictions or pornography.

Yet in physical addictions such as alcoholism, many of these same causes and behavioral patterns are still at work.

In either case, hypnosis is an instrument that the mind can use to address addiction-related thoughts and behaviors. Hypnotherapy may be an important addition to an extensive package of treatments under the close guidance of an addiction counselor.

CHAPTER 10

POSITIVE AFFIRMATIONS TO USE IN DRUG ADDICTION TREATMENT

Positive affirmations are assertions that can help fight negative thinking. We encourage clients to make use of positive affirmations to help them make meaningful life changes. Positive words are simply reminding you of all the positive things about you, and motivating you to move on in difficult times.

How Positive Affirmations Work?

Saying good things about yourself prepares the brain for improvement. Studies show that making positive changes is easier with the use of positive affirmations. Using positive affirmations changes your neuroplasticity or the science of redirecting your brain to different thought patterns.

Below are 100 effective claims to use in treating drug addiction:

1. I can do it.

2. I get stronger each day.

3. I was not made to surrender.

4. My power is greater than any fight.

5. I want to be who I am.

6. I am developing myself every day.

7. I discovered I am tough.

8. I know what I'm worth.

9. I inspire people

10. I choose what I want to become.

11. I have decided I'm fine enough.

12. I have decided I'm worth it.

13. I am bold enough to do so.

14. No challenge is too big for me to tackle.

15. I can turn my story around.

16. Like me it's not their job, it's mine.

17. I use a defect as a stepping stone.

18. I have the courage to say 'no.'

19. I'm really smart.

20. I'm blessed.

21. I am stronger than any storm.

22. I deserve to make my dreams come true.

23. I deserve true love.

24. I deserve joy.

25. Unconditional love is part of me.

26. I deserve respect.

27. I salute with strength every day.

28. I can handle it, no matter what comes my way.

29. I am not afraid.

30. I do believe in myself.

31. I believe in my know-how

32. Today is my day.

33. Today I am changing my life.

34. I am loved.

35. It will fill me with unlimited energy today.

36. Today I am a magnet of blessing.

37. Today I am a giver of love.

38. Now I'm going to learn and develop.

39. Today I would be a happier person than I was yesterday.

40. I will find myself succeeding today.

41. My addiction is heavy, but I'm stronger.

42. I am thankful for the light of another day.

43. Now I'm going to be fearless.

44. Yesterday I did my utmost.

45. What I have achieved today leads to a better tomorrow.

46. My heart is just pure.

47. I am proud of myself.

48. Tomorrow is a brand-new day full of possibilities.

49. The world is a wonderful place.

50. I enjoy sharing what I have.

51. I am known for my kindness and my strength.

52. I am amazed by what my body can do.

53. I am more strong than negative thoughts.

54. I accept my individuality.

55. I am not wrong

56. I dedicate myself completely to achieving my goals.

57. I've got enough; I do enough, I'm enough.

58. My life is a gift, and I'll use that gift with trust and joy.

59. I deserve compassion, understanding, and empathy.

60. I choose confidence above fear.

61. I build my life just the way I want it.

62. I settle for being optimistic.

63. I feel at peace with whom I am.

64. I matter.

65. I am acting courageously and with confidence.

66. I can live my life as an exciting adventure.

67. I live in the moment, and I take steps to ensure a glorious future.

68. I turn my dreams into goals, my priorities into steps, and my steps into practice.

69. I am keen to improve for the better.

70. I am capable of making my greatest desires manifest.

71. Anything amazing will happen.

72. I allow love to fill me up and lead me in everything I do.

73. My mind is firmly free and open to possibilities.

74. I am turning into the best version of myself.

75. I can do anything I put my mind to.

76. I have the confidence to carry on.

77. I make a living out of my dreams.

78. I have complete responsibility for my life.

79. I will achieve whatever I put my mind to.

80. My energy brings forth my truth. What I am focused on, I'm going to manifest.

81. I am linked with the infinite abundance of the universe.

82. I make my own meaningful decisions.

83. I love myself and embrace me.

84. Good stuff happens to me all the time.

85. I'm productive every single day.

86. I am well respected.

87. Today I'm going to try the positive at every moment.

88. I love to adjust; it gives me opportunities.

89. I am on the way to fulfilling my dreams.

90. I am capable.

91. I am stronger than any illegal drug.

92. I have the confidence to do something positive.

93. I do not wish to give up on myself.

94. I am purposeful.

95. I was made with divine intention.

96. I can, I will, and I can.

97. I cultivate my soul.

98. I am responsible for the way I look today.

99. I choose and don't wait to be chosen.

100.   "I'm enough"

Such 100 optimistic statements are the ideal complement to our services for treating addiction.

We support clients with a drug or alcohol addiction through

multiple comprehensive treatments and therapeutic experiences that can bring purpose to their lives. Drug therapy doesn't have to be intense; you set yourself up for success by tempering your negative feelings with positive affirmations. These affirmations are also perfect for any family or friends in treatment who have a loved one. We encourage clients in our treatment centers to make use of positive affirmations to rewire their brains for positivity.

CHAPTER 11

THERAPEUTIC ACTIVITIES TO TAKE

AFTER REHAB

30 Therapeutic recuperation exercises to do

Many specific exercises have a tremendous therapeutic benefit, making them an ideal tool to be used while you seek addiction treatment. As a way of communicating with yourself, your emotions, and those around you, you should perform these activities. Using skills learned in our treatment options in the short-term vs long-term abstinence can make a difference. We are experts in the treatment of alcohol and opioid abuse, using proven effective methods of managing abuse.

In addition to how to avoid a relapse, our services teach a new way of life. The recovery services use therapeutic strategies, including exercise therapy, to foster healthier behaviors rather than inappropriate ones.

Treatment for drug or alcohol addiction should always provide coping skills to be used as a means to manage stressors or cravings. Also, behavioral therapies, family counseling, and community therapies can be used to improve the healing process and encourage self-expression.

Our treatment services improve mental wellbeing when treating drug use problems with a holistic approach to mind, body, and spiritual care.

They can be used to recover from anxiety, work through emotion, and replace unhealthy behaviors. They believe in the power of healing mind, body, and spirit for complete recovery at Royal Life Centers. You can improve emotionally, physically, and spiritually by doing these therapeutic exercises, and you can find pleasure in doing so!

Here are 30 rehabilitation exercises to be carried out in and out of recuperation:

1. Coloring

It is a therapeutic activity to use coloring books that can calm the mind by allowing it to focus on something simple. Alcoholics and addicts will also struggle with a surge of feelings during rehabilitation, using a coloring book helps give the mind something really easy to concentrate on.

2. Journaling

Journaling has considerable therapeutic value. Journaling is not only beneficial at the moment, but it helps one to better understand the modes of thought and their emotions. In the recovery process, journaling is very helpful, as it often allows the alcoholic or addict to see where they are mentally and emotionally.

3. Painting

Painting is rather calming, as it also helps us to concentrate purely on what they do. Any activity that enables artistic expression is useful for recuperation.

4. Listen to music

Music can alter or boost the mood, and it's a perfect tool for those in recovery. Feel good music is motivating and has been scientifically proven to offer emotional support to those in drug care.

5. Collaging / Scrapbooking

Creating a collage can help those in rehabilitation, as it can increase productivity. Starting and finishing a project can be a strong motivating factor. Visual, emotional relations may become a form of self-expression.

6. Knitting

Knitting is therapeutic in its ability to reinforce sensory-motor function, allowing one to concentrate on what they do with methodical repetition. Creation of any kind is advantageous for recovery.

7. Create a "Calm Down" Jar

The creation and enjoyment of a "calm down" jar is a therapeutic process. You may make one of these jars from containers for household products, including a glass or plastic bottle, pan, or any clear container. All you need to make is tiny items like glitter, plastic pieces, stars, figurines, dice, marbles, etc.

Just place the items inside the jar, and fill the jar with water, to make a "calm down" jar. You can add food coloring to change the liquid color of the jar. Place the lid tightly on the jar once it is full, and glue it down. Shake the pot, watch the objects float through the liquid, and turn it upside down. This activity is very soothing, both for creating and looking at.

8. Play Games

Challenges such as 21 questions, I-Spy, etc. are perfect for enhancing cognitive memory, and also for increasing one's concentration on the job. Such games are therapeutic, and among those playing, they often develop communication skills.

9. Draw Mandalas

Mandalas are circular drawings inside a series of circles that consist of repetitive designs. Focus and calm down by concentrating on one design at a time, as a therapeutic tool of tolerance of distress.

10. Create a "Worry Box."

Tactile activities that allow creative self-expression are extremely beneficial for both awareness and stress tolerance. You should prepare for the therapeutic activity by purchasing a small wooden box and crafting supplies. Decorate the box with ink, paper, glitter, etc. Use the box to house any symbolic items or pieces of paper inscribed on them with "worries."

This activity is quite common for the treatment of trauma

sufferers. Commonly used as a guided meditation exercise, physically creating a safe box to store your "unwanted" emotions or concerns in, will bring a visual counter piece to the emotional management activity. This activity aims to offer clients the feeling they are in charge of their worries and emotions.

11. Go for a Stroll

Going out for a walk is an undervalued way of clearing your mind and exercising mindfulness. Start going for a walk and focus on your climate. What would you like to see? Which color to each tree are the leaves? Passing grass patches or flowers? Clouds in the sky?

12. Cooking

Cooking is beneficial as it not only promotes speech but also facilitates awareness of the sensory information associated with cooking. Cooking is also a satisfying process, as you put your effort into it and are rewarded with a meal. Cooking is a healthy therapeutic activity, as it also teaches us that doing something good for ourselves, like feeding our bodies, can help us to relax too.

13. Meditate

Meditation is the practice of silencing the mind of any distractions, focusing on your well-being for a few moments or minutes. Meditation has many advantages, including spiritual growth. Try to sit on the floor and focus on how your body feels in that moment. Is there any tension over there? Visualize the tension with each deep breath easing itself. One may also use guided meditations to help meditation and attain a relaxing state.

14. Play with Clay

Given the satisfaction it provides to have power over the material in your hands, finding time to play with clay or play dough is therapeutic. Would you like to form the material into some given shape? Perhaps just strain out the substance to relieve tension. Keeping your hands busy can help with the tolerance of distress, and the possibilities of molding a material foster self-expression.

15. Construct with Kinetic Sand

Building something with kinetic sand allows you to remain mindful by focusing on the material sensation in your hands. Any activity which promotes development healthily is also therapeutic.

16. Do a Sudoku or Crossword Puzzle

Hold the mind focused on a crossword puzzle or Sudoku, which not only enhances cognitive performance but also helps the participant to concentrate on one target at a time and give them small rewards along the way.

17. Create a Dreamcatcher

Creating dreamcatchers is a perfect way to experience serenity. Dreamcatchers are representative of an object that, while you are sleeping, catches negative thoughts and energies to protect against negativity. Creating a dreamcatcher can be a calming activity as a sign of security which also gives a deeper meaning to the creator.

18. Write a Letter

Sitting down to write a letter is a therapeutic tool because it helps the person to reflect on their feelings in a manner that will create something that they care about. If you want to send the message or not, writing down your true thoughts and feelings to someone else is also a beneficial task.

19. Progressive Relaxation of Muscles

Progressive relaxation of the muscle is an extremely useful technique, both for relaxation and as a sleeping method. The way it works focuses on how each muscle feels, beginning with your head and moving down to your toes. Concentrate on how every part of your body feels when you step imaginatively downwards. Visualize your focus on each muscle as you make a cognitive choice to relax that part of your body before moving on.

20. Write a List of Gratitude

Making a list is a great way to concentrate your attention on a single subject. This is a great way to control thoughts about racing by focusing on one topic to guide your thought train. Writing a list of thanks, or a list of things for which you are grateful is a therapeutic practice that promotes gratitude and positivity. This is an active way of focusing on the positive things in life, particularly when you feel down.

21. Origami

Origami, or the Japanese paper-folding art, is a therapeutic activity that brings cognitive-motor functions into action. Origami is therapeutic since, before your eyes, a series of small motions can come to life.

22. Make a Cup of Tea

A therapeutic practice is both making a cup of tea and drinking it. The process of making a cup of tea is systematic, which helps the mind to focus on small tasks at a time. The scent of the tea, the feeling of the mug in your mouth, the taste of the tea, and the sight of the steam rising from the cup are all part of mindfulness.

23. Ripping Paper

The cutting of paper can be used as a way to alleviate tension or anxiety by enabling the mind to concentrate on something "mindless." Ripping paper is calming and can be a mental help for those in rehabilitation to imagine their stressors or problems being "repressed."

24. Read a Book

Reading constitutes a very therapeutic practice. It allows those in recovery to get lost in another world, to recognize other perspectives, to visualize something else, etc. Reading is a great tool for distracting, practicing distress tolerance, and for the moment, encouraging a focus on something else.

25. Squeeze a Stress Ball

An old coping exercise but an important one in times of

depression is using a stress ball to pinch. Focusing your attention on a tactile item can be of enormous therapeutic value in recovery.

26. Play with a Fidgeting Device

Fidget spinners and fidget cubes are becoming increasingly popular, and are extremely helpful for those with anxiety. In moments of distress, these devices allow a sensory connection, which teaches those in recovery to stay in the present moment and also teaches tolerance.

27. Watch Comedy

Whether it's a show or a film, watching something light-hearted can be a relaxing experience that can relax in times of depression and provide a completely different emotion. Usually watching a comedy can cause laughter, which releases good chemicals in your brain.

28. Do a Puzzle

Working on a puzzle will enhance cognitive performance, which helps those in rehabilitation to work at their speed on something. It is beneficial for those in recovery to have a clear goal in mind to do a productive task, with small rewards along the way that encourages them to keep going.

29. Boardgames

Playing a board game implicitly teaches others how to improve their skills and interpersonal performance in team building. Having a shared aim

30. Take a Bubble Bath

Taking a hot shower is a sensory experience that encourages relaxation and sensitivity. Hydrotherapy is also a highly useful therapeutic tool for recovery, particularly during medical detoxification, to ease the symptoms of discomforts withdrawal.

ADOPTING A DRUG-FREE LIFESTYLE

Develop a Drug-Free Lifestyle for Abstinence

If you're trying to maintain long-term abstinence from alcohol or drugs, it's important to develop a drug-free lifestyle in all aspects of your life — at home, at work, and during your leisure time.

If you have been pursuing treatment for your alcohol or substance addiction from a skilled recovery clinic, one of the most important purposes of your ongoing or follow-up care is to help you learn to substitute your past unhealthy habits with safer and more successful alternatives.

Assisting friends and family

One of the first steps toward developing a drug-free lifestyle is to avoid those people who were directly involved in your former lifestyle of drinking or drug-using, those who helped you get drugs, use drugs, or were your drinking buddies. Many addicts find that they must develop new friendships, social patterns, and recreational activities to develop a substance-free lifestyle.

Your rehabilitation counselor will try to help you identify drug-free supportive friends and family members and encourage you to improve those relationships and take part in recreational activities with them, to replace the time you spent looking for and using drugs. If you don't have drug-free friends or loved ones, your counselor will encourage you to get involved with new social groups and make supportive new friends.

Developing a Structured Timetable

Another significant aspect of maintaining a drug-free lifestyle is the maintenance of a regular daily routine that is easily followable. In your life, order and organization can be your best friends in recovery while your adversary can be a lifestyle that is chaotic and disorganized.

When you were in your recovery program's early abstinence period, your counselor probably worked with you to set up a routine and/or weekly schedule to help you start structuring your time and reducing your substance hunting by using healthier alternatives to activities. It is crucial not to leave the organized schedule or deviate from it regularly in the maintenance abstinence phase of your recovery.

Developing Wider, More Substantial Goals

While maintaining your abstinence remains a high priority in your life, it is helpful to identify larger goals for your future to develop a drug-free lifestyle long term. Now that you've accomplished more than 90 days of abstinence, you're likely to start developing larger, long-term goals like going back to school, changing career paths, or saving towards financial goals.

Helping you build and sustain a drug-free lifestyle will play an important role in defining certain goals for your life and creating a strategy to achieve those goals. Within the framework of your new treatment lifestyle, your follow-up advisor will help you understand how to move towards these goals.

Developing Spirituality

You were also exposed to the idea of spirituality, which has little to do with religious rituals or dogma if you took it as part of your recovery plan in a 12-step clinic. Spirituality, as it applies to heal, involves cultivating beliefs and setting altruistic aspirations in your life — seeking satisfaction and happiness beyond yourself.

In any successful recovery program, spirituality can be an important factor. It involves connecting to a power that extends beyond everyday concerns. Your counselor will encourage you to engage in "greater than yourself " efforts such as doing service work for your support group, getting more involved in your religious organization, doing community service or volunteering for charitable work.

Your counselor won't try to define any "higher power" for you — that will be left entirely to you. Research has shown that developing a drug-free lifestyle can be enhanced by relating to a power that is transcendent and greater than yourself.

CHAPTER 12
HELPING A FAMILY MEMBER COPE
WITH DRUG ADDICTION

1. GET EDUCATED ABOUT DRUG ADDICTION

Take the time to learn more about substance dependency development and behavior. Addiction is much more than the misuse of substances such as cocaine, alcohol, marijuana, or prescription medications. It may be a behavior that is usually caused by some underlying emotional issue, chemical imbalance, or other disorder that causes a person to act or self-medicate in a certain way.

Individuals with these habits can be unhealthily addicted to just about everything – whether it's sex, exercise, work, eating, or a drug.

So, when someone is addicted to something, often other disorders like depression, anxiety, bipolar, obsessive-compulsiveness or eating disorders are there.

Whenever a person is addicted to a drug or activity, the continued use and abuse becomes all about stability rather than getting "happy." As time goes by, the perceived advantages of the action or drug that originally tempted them usually fades away, but the need and desire remains.

Treatment services such as drug recovery aim to resolve the root causes of addictive behaviors. This is why the prevention of drug abuse can be so influential in bringing about life-altering habits and productive, positive changes.

2. OFFER SUPPORT BUT DO NOT ENABLE

Encouraging the addiction of a family member comes in many ways, some of which you do not consider encouraging, but are. Recognizing the behaviors and actions you and your family are performing that allow your drug-addicted loved one to remain in this destructive state, is important.

Enabling can be anything from allowing the addicted family member to stay in your home and abuse drugs or going on with such habits while there, or it may be something as easy as making excuses for the offender.

It can seem like a very cruel act to deny someone you love basic treatment or dignity. But knowing your encouraging conduct takes a lot of compassion, and taking action to avoid it. These actions can ultimately help your loved one get back on the road to recovery. An awareness that now is not the time for blame is just as crucial as acknowledging encouraging behavior. Now it's time to act.

3. AVOID FINANCIALLY SUPPORTING THE ADDICTION

This is likewise a form of enabling, and it rears its head in various ways. When a drug-addicted family member asks you for money, have your bills paid, or even lives in your rent-free home, their addiction can be supported by this.

Your loved one may give you many reasons for asking you for money, but sadly all paths are likely to financially support the substance abuse.

4. ESTABLISH BOUNDARIES AND STICK TO THEM

Once you have decided that you will no longer take part in the drug addiction of your loved one – that you will no longer allow them because you love them, yourself, and your family too much – then you have to set boundaries.

Possibly one of the toughest things to do to get to that level. It is just as hard to enforce those boundaries. Next, see to it that the limits are practical. Are you willing to cross any boundaries that you set?

Second, it's also important to know why you are setting boundaries. If the boundary is set to protect you and your family, that's a healthier motive than using the boundary to attempt to control or change the addicted family member's behavior.

Whatever limits you set, know that your loved one can respond to these limits in various ways, and "sticking to your guns" can be highly emotional.

5. TO HELP THEM, YOU MUST HELP YOURSELF FIRST

You may not know this, but the healing and recovery process is just as much for your loved one as it is for you and your family. Drug addiction has different effects on family relationships and addict / alcoholic family members in different ways.

Emotions and attitudes that accompany the dependency run deep within a family. For everyone in the recovery process, the complicated nature of addiction can require education and therapy.

We always recommend the participation of family members in our family program. Once the client has completed treatment with drug addiction, we recommend that the family continue to work with support programs through organizations such as Al-Anon, Nar-anon, Alateen, Co-Dependents Anonymous, as well as family therapy forms when needed.

6. DON'T LET STRUGGLES OF THE ADDICTION TAKE OVER YOUR LIFE

Sometimes the addiction of a loved one that consumes your life to the point that it swallows you and your entire family. You should also support the addict/alcoholic in your family when taking care of yourself and other family members who might still be caught up in the situation. You do this by maintaining your daily life, your job, and your interests; taking time to take care of yourself.

Consider engaging yourself, first in community support groups such as the organizations we described earlier (Al-Anon and the like). You should take a look at counseling. Talking to someone helps. These things can help you get a better understanding of how to cope with your family and protect them. Remember, their addiction is not your fault. Do your best, and you will be there.

7. AVOID LECTURING / GUILT / INTIMIDATION AS A WAY COPING

An addiction is a condition that needs medical support, guidance, and a lot of research to discover the root causes of the behavior. Often complex family relationships and issues are a factor in destructive behavior.

Having your loved one feel hurt, frightened, or humiliated can only aggravate the situation and trigger a spiral of more self-medication, particularly if the person is not willing to accept that they have a problem. Drug treatment requires love, support, and empathy but also willingness.

8. LOOK INTO DRUG REHAB SERVICES FOR AND LOOK INTO PROFESSIONAL TREATMENT

Your loved one probably doesn't even know where to get started, or what options are there for help. They probably might not even want to hear about them.

If they aren't ready for a change, they are likely to shoot down any option that you present, they can simply find it too exhausting to have to study their choices.

This is where you can be of service by first seeing what's out there for treatment, so when the time is right, you can make educated suggestions. There are many treatment methods, and it's important to keep this in mind before selecting a drug rehabilitation facility to explore.

The 12-step program is one of the most popular methods. We at Cirque Lodge believe that each addiction and individual is unique, and we tailor treatment accordingly.

So, while we're based on the 12-step approach, we also integrate effective forms of clinical therapy into a mind, body, and spirit approach to help a person get healthy from within. Learning alternatives to treatment is the secret to the wellbeing of your loved one in the program.

There's always an alternative to supporting someone in a downward spiral that you think needs to seek treatment very soon, whether they want to or not. That's called interference. Interventions can require preparation, as there are several layers to staging it successfully.

If you believe you need an intervention for your loved one, it's recommended that you speak with a professional. We can help you with information from many of the leading interventionists available regarding intervention services.

9. ENCOURAGE THEM TO SEEK HELP

Confidence is a key factor in this step. In Step 7, we talked about replacing fear and shame with love and encouragement. If that method has been developed, then encouragement comes next.

While some drug rehabilitation centers and support groups use the "tough love" approach, we believe with encouragement that you can get just as far or further. At this level, you might ask yourself, how can you love and promote while at the same time setting limits and first looking out for yourself?

When healthy boundaries are set, and you put yourself first, you can share love and empathy more freely. You made the decision not to allow that person to harm you or to take advantage of you, or whatever the boundary you set.

Once you have taken a back seat with any negative feelings and emotions about the person or situation, you can start taking a more objective approach to the problem and motivate them to begin getting help.

10. BE INVOLVED IN THE DRUG REHAB TREATMENT AND RECOVERY

Everyone must recover from alcoholism and drug addiction. If a drug-addicted family member is on the path to rehabilitation because you or the family have not taken steps to become part of the healing process, this may potentially impede your loved one's progress. Help is important during that process. The use of a family plan and counseling can be a way to facilitate the healing process.

Addiction is often deep-seated in family issues and learned behaviors that derive from inside the home. If an addicted person attempts to break the cycle and change their behavior, it is very difficult if the family hasn't also started to work through their issues surrounding the home problems.

CHAPTER 13

NEW POSITIVE HABITS TO HELP WHILE RECOVERING FROM DRUG ADDICTION

9 Ways to Develop Healthy Habits

1. Start slowly

Ease your way into new ways of living. Although diving right into it can be tempting, it's recommended that you start slowly and then build up.

At this point, your goal is to determine the habit. You want to get familiar with your new habit and start to fit it into your routine. Start with 10, instead of doing 100 push-ups every day. Instead of overhauling your whole diet, simply add one vegetable to every meal. Smaller acts take less thinking, and less effort is needed. Once these actions become consistent, they will then begin to feel more natural. They'll soon become a normal part of your everyday routine.

2. Don't Rock the Boat

If you prefer visual indications, then this tip is smooth sailing.

Creates a visual reminder of your habit using a physical

calendar and a marker. Pin the calendar to your wall or place it on your desk, and draw an "X" on that day in your calendar whenever you complete your task for the day. You will have a steady flow in a few days. Your only task from there is remaining afloat and not moving the ships.

3. Be Clear

Implement your actions with total clarity. Vague statements like "I'm going to try to write 500 words a day," aren't effective.

To maximize your chances of following through with your new behaviors, you need to state clearly where and when they will happen. Here are two useful ways of getting this done:

- Linking: Connect your new habit to an activity you have set up. For example, "I'll pack a healthy lunch before I go to bed."

- Scheduling: Pacing your new habit. For example, if you're trying to improve your writing skills, schedule a "writing appointment," where you'll sit down and write for a specified period.

4. Reward Yourself

Be proud of their accomplishments. Not only is your success being celebrated important to your encouragement, but it also makes you feel good. These empowering feelings of accomplishment and pride will inspire you to do more and create even greater success.

But rewards don't have to be expensive. It might be something small, such as visiting a movie theatre, spending time with your significant other, or taking a relaxing bubble bath.

Make feeling good about yourself a priority. Every step, however small this may be, is a step in the right direction.

5. Eliminate Obstacles

Make the process easier. If eating healthier is one of your goals, then keeping a cookie jar on your kitchen counter will only undermine your efforts. Replace the cookie jar with a colorful fruit bowl, instead. Essentially this will help to improve the climate and increase the chances of success.

When you eliminate the obstacles, your new habits are more likely to remain.

6. Use your Social Web

Friends and other supportive individuals can help keep you on track.

Good habits are traits that have a powerful impact on your behavior. If you are inspired to pursue your dreams and visions but are surrounded by pessimists and naysayers, it's time to expand your social circle. Connect with others who share the same passion and desire to be productive too.

7. Commit Yourself to This

Become committed to your new habits. For example, it can be very enticing to hurry home after a long and stressful day at work – rather than going to the gym, as you had initially planned. Yet, if you had told a friend you'd meet, then refusing makes things harder.

By sticking to your new habits, it keeps you responsible for your choices and gives you an extra boost when things get tough.

8. Think Long Term

The twenty-first-day theory is just a myth. There's no specific amount of time needed to construct a habit. Short-term fixes, such as seven-day cleanses or 21-day challenges, are meant to produce quick results, but they are not sustainable.

How long do healthy habits take to form? As long as you need. The aim is to create positive change, which can be accomplished by "short-term tasks" and "long-term goals."

Your goals are the bigger goals and dreams you want to accomplish, whilst your tasks are the daily activities you complete to make your goals come true. For example, publishing your first book could be one of your aims, and contacting a new agent would be the corresponding daily task.

Tasks make your ambitious goals seem closer. It's just a matter of time, and consistency before you reach your goal.

9. Make it Personal

This is about you above all. You have to believe in every moment that your new habits are part of your identity. Strengthen this notion with statements or statements such as "I am the kind of person that takes my mental well-being seriously. I must meditate every day for ten minutes."

Repeat and fully understand those comments regularly. They will eventually become a part of you.

Stick to Your Habits

You will be getting a little closer to your goals each day. You just have to start going forward.

If you find keeping healthy habits hard, don't be discouraged. By shifting your mindset strategically, you can start putting yourself in the right direction, and getting those habits to stick. Our Building an Iron Self-Discipline Journey, will help you learn how to stick to your routines and empower yourself.

CHAPTER 14
THE 30 DAYS DRUG-FREE CHALLENGE

MONDAY: Day 1

So, you think you have what it takes to have 30-day alcohol-free time? Great, because we do that too – and we have plenty of health tips and tricks to help you stop drinking alcohol and get you fitter and happier.

TUESDAY: Day 2

Your first booze-free 24 hours flew by! Now you're on a roll, try to embrace the power of 3 by treating your body with two more health-kicks: grab some water, snack on five fruits or veg, take a walk or get an early night. Do not use your sober month as an excuse for bad eating, while sugar treats may seem less harmful than alcohol; they are not a healthy substitute.

Go into this challenge with the mindset that your body is a temple. If you're looking for a fresh, healthier drink in an evening to tickle your taste buds, try seven awesome superfood smoothies-they're most delicious, no alcohol required.

WEDNESDAY: Day 3

Ditching your beer or wine-fix after-work doesn't have to be all doom and gloom. Every day you manage to get booze-free, reward yourself with the amount you would normally have spent on a beer in the bar or a glass of wine in front of the TV. According to Macmillan Cancer Support, the average Briton spends £50,000 throughout their lifetime on alcohol in the UK alone, reports The Independent. Even for a modest drinker, that's pretty pricey.

As a bonus, treat yourself to a new piggy bank and add sober extra cash to the pot that you've saved. Imagine what all of that money you will buy with!

THURSDAY: Day 4

You won't believe this challenge can bring physical and mental transformation. Alcohol has a lot to answer for and shows it to your body. Do you have dark circles under your eyes? By reducing quick eye movement (REM) sleep, booze will stop you from getting a good night's kip. Alcohol also massively dehydrates the skin, leaving it dull, irritated, and even flaky to your touch.

You can forget about feeling exhausted and unmotivated and look forward to a shiny, radiant complexion, thanks to the 30-day challenge. It's well worth taking a picture before and after or keeping a progress diary. Your face tells a lot about your diet and exercise habits. Let's see what yours is saying about you.

FRIDAY: Day 5

Is your 30-day challenge triggering weight loss? Some forget how many empty calories are in alcohol (which converts straight into stubborn fat!) A 22-ounce bottle of beer is equal to the same number of calories as a large slice of pizza, at around 180-200 calories a bottle. Five glasses in, and you're already around the 1000 calorie mark, and that's late at night. Famously, alcohol increases your appetite and will tempt you to reach for kebabs, chips, and pizza.

If you're being good or slimming down for a special event, it will pay off to take a break from booze. If alcohol has played a large role in your diet before the challenge, the pounds will fly away.

SATURDAY: Day 6

When it comes to meeting the mission, weekends are the hardest. The last thing you want to do when calling on Friday night is reached for a bottle. Take this 30-day experiment seriously, and be surprised by sipping on a cheeky mocktail or two.

They're extremely delicious, they come filled with health benefits, and they miss the hangover. Can we seduce you? You don't need to have a good time with alcohol, and we can prove that. Forget to load up on cosmos, play bartender, and try to mix a free 'Raspberry Fizz' booze. You'll love it!

SUNDAY: Day 7

Congrats. You hit the booze-free 7-day mark; give yourself a big pat on the back. Now you are past the first hurdle, here is a brief reminder of all the wonderful work you've done. There are so many health benefits coming along your way, get ready for it: a healthy complexion, greater concentration, and productivity, inches off your waist, better sleep, and all-round fitter.

When you are wondering whether or not to go to the bar, remember why you are undertaking this challenge and what awesome advantages you can achieve as a result.

MONDAY: Day 8

What keeps you motivated? If you're struggling to see the good in completing this task, really dig deep and write down five reasons why it's important to you to go 30 days sober. Have you taken it up to boost your wellbeing, save some cash, sleep better, become a better employee or a family, friend, or partner who needs you to go the extra mile and beat the bad habit?

Whatever the cause, use it to inspire you to complete your mission. When you're busy with family life and work-life, it's easy to lose focus, and sometimes achieving 30 days of soberness doesn't seem worth extra effort, but trust us when we say it is!

Push forward and hold on to that, you can. Each accomplishment starts with the decision to try it out.

TUESDAY: Day 9

Craving a tipple? You could eat a small snack or meal for the number of calories that you would normally consume drinking a 22-ounce glass of beer or a large glass of wine. Get a savory pop from some sweet potato fries or satisfy your sweet tooth with a handful of cocoa and coconut bites, they're both deliciously tasty and calorie-free.

WEDNESDAY: Day 10

Have you ever thought of adding more value to your objective? Don't shy away from talking about your fantastic advances. Inspire others to follow suit, or perhaps better, raise contributions in the name of a major cause. If you have a reputation as a party person and your friends don't think you're going to have a chance to go sober, tell them to put their money where their mouth is and raise money for charity.

Being 30-day booze-free is a fantastic accomplishment and something you should be immensely proud of. Do not hang back at the bar, order loud and proud, "tap water." and rake in the extra pennies along the way for a deserving charity.

THURSDAY: Day 11

Studies from Sussex University showed that people who could give up alcohol for one month would decrease the amount they drink in the long term, which eventually decreases the risk of developing conditions like cardiovascular disease, depression, and dementia.

A healthier, much happier you, so take the bull by the horns and take this amazing opportunity to the fullest. In reality, what looks like an innocent drink can be pretty harmful, but there's still time to cut down bad habits and make a change.

As Shakespeare once said, "holding our fate is not in the stars but ourselves." Stop waiting, and give the 30-day challenge all you have.

FRIDAY: DAY 12

Wait a second, where's the hangover? It suits you for a sober weekend. If a recent booze-free evening with drunken friends turned out to be unbearable, or you're dreading the city's imminent sober night – step back and put things into perspective.

We get it, it can be hard work to go booze-free while the drunken world is against you, but you are made up of great stuff, and we believe you have the courage to see it through. Keeping sober is possible on special occasions! Well, you can do just that!

SATURDAY: Day 13

Forget about FOMO and get ready for a 'me' moment. A cozy night-in, catch up on your latest box set is worth skipping the city for a night. Resting on the weekend not only gives your wallet a break, but it also allows your mind and body time to recover after a hard week at the office, not to mention 'quality time' with your friends, family, or other half.

Ladies, leave the sky-high heels to one side; fellas put the aftershave down, and snuggle up for a well-deserved night-in on the settee instead.

SUNDAY: DAY 14

Two weeks in-how do you feel? You should already notice that your skin looks healthier; you are more relaxed and hopefully enjoying a sound night's sleep. Behind the scenes, being away from the alcohol for 14 days will leave the liver in a much healthier shape. Also, the challenge breaks down your alcohol tolerance, so you don't become addicted to the substance.

If you look in the mirror and fail to see results, talk to a friend you haven't seen for a while. You see yourself daily, so it's hard to notice any changes to your look. Or if you don't already have a booze-free diary, keep track of where you're up to.

MONDAY: DAY 15

Stay solid and invincible in the face of social activities, don't give up! It isn't worth it to let everything you've learned go to waste for one booze-fueled night. The challenge of 30 days can work, but only if you commit.

Sort your Strategy for the weekend. Before heading out on a booze-free night out, tell yourself you're not going to touch a drop, even though the amount of peer pressure you're facing reaches record levels, you're better. Remember why you are doing this; the slimmer waist, the smoother skin, the happier, the fitter, the more successful you.

TUESDAY: DAY 16

Do you know what you've been drinking? There's some glamour attached to alcohol and intense drinking, but quickly shifts when you know what's in your drink. A 22-ounce glass of cider contains about 21 grams of sugar, reports The Telegraph, and carries about 210 calories – the equivalent of swigging two single cream shots. Not nice. But if you don't drink sugar-laden beverages and stick to the alcohol, mixers have calories, and then there's the takeaway ride ...

If your friends have a lot to say about your decision to stay booze-free, remind them of the junk with which they fuel their body. That's going to keep them quiet!

WEDNESDAY: DAY 17

Negativity engenders negativity. If you have people in your friendship group who can't understand your decision to go booze-free, try avoiding them. It's hard enough to beat bad habits without making those closest to you feel guilty about wanting to improve yourself. You should have friends there to love you, no matter what.

Continue the good work and don't be distracted by your bad feeling. Instead, they're charmed to take up the challenge themselves. It makes it much easier to have a mate to share the excitement with. Work your magic, it is worth its weight in gold to have a sober partner in crime through this challenge.

THURSDAY: DAY 18

You can rehydrate the skin and skip the alcohol toxins by stopping the booze and topping up on H2O. Alcohol, as we know, damages the liver, which plays a key role in detoxifying chemicals and purifying the blood. If booze starts messing with the working of the liver, the skin is the first to reveal it, leaving you gaunt, pasty, and full of pores.

You are bringing your liver and skin back to life by replacing those cheeky drinks with sparkling water. Drink as much water as you can for the best results during the day!

FRIDAY: DAY 19

Who is missing out on a hangover? You don't. The sickness, the headache, the shakes, the anxiety, the regret; this is the worst possible affliction at that moment. You wouldn't wish your worst enemy this sort of agony, and it never hurries away. Some fortunate people get rewarded with a hangover for 2 days or more.

The body is dehydrated, the stomach is irritated, your sugar levels are all over the place, and you have no chance of getting a night's sleep that is good quality. Who would pay for this sort of pain? It sounds like a lot of people, but you know better. Thank goodness, you no longer need to worry about this.

SATURDAY: DAY 20

This challenge is 100% in the mind, and it's an amazing test of your self-discipline. Not many people have been able to beat the temptation as you have, and although they may not admit it; they may wish they could. Naturally, this kind of strength and commitment will move to other areas of your life, your lifestyle, your job, your relationships, and because of that, you will become a better / happier person.

Being booze-free will not be a big deal long enough, and you will be searching for the next opportunity. It's addictive, you get an amazing sense of achievement from smashing goals and hitting personal targets. You're doing well, accept it and keep pushing forwards!

Don't quit

SUNDAY: DAY 21

Are you feeling better in yourself? This is probably because, for an amazing 21 days, you've been sober. You've made it through most of the challenge and overcome the difficult obstacles, so why stop now? If you have had three weeks without a single drop of booze, you can take on the world.

Give your body a chance to fight, to be the best it can be. Make it to the end of the 30-day challenge, and you will be able to reduce blood glucose levels by 16 percent, reducing the risk of type 2 diabetes and heart disease. What a perfect beginning, don't hesitate!

MONDAY: DAY 22

Sleep well tonight! Going for a month alcohol-free can improve your sleep by an incredible ten percent+. When busy lives get in the way, we often forget what it feels like to get a good night's sleep, but there are so many benefits to the early night. It increases your memory, brightens your mood, and makes your skin look radiant.

There is a common misconception that getting a couple of drinks before bedtime will help you get a good night's sleep when it has the opposite effect. This causes you to wake up much earlier than usual and ruins your sleep, leaving you with headache, cold sweats, and bad dreams as well. Stick to chamomile tea, this is the best option for beauty sleep.

TUESDAY: DAY 23

Join your efforts on the challenge with a natural high. Most resort to alcohol to alleviate tension. But alcohol is never the solution, it's a depressant. There are far better ways to relieve stress, and they do not involve drinking a bucket load of booze, as attractive as it might look like, an evening spent slurring your words, and stumbling home. Why not get a nice endorphin boost from a post-work run, or by taking a dip at the local pool, in line with the new, healthier you?

WEDNESDAY: DAY 24

Bye-bye cerebral fog. Hopefully, you will be feeling the benefits of your challenge by now. Going alcohol-free for five weeks will improve job efficiency by 17 percent and wakefulness by 9.5 percent, according to New Scientist!

When you have a heavy night in town, the central nervous system takes a direct hit, which often makes itself known through slurred words, slow reaction times, and poor balance. Repeated bingeing on booze inevitably exacerbates these effects, including post-hangover, contributing to what is widely called 'brain fog.' Alcohol-free living will dramatically minimize that feeling, leaving you healthy, concentrated, and ready for a productive day.

THURSDAY: DAY 25

Are you feeling a little baggier in your trousers? Dropped the size of a dress? You'll find yourself a few pounds lighter by drinking less. Evening wine drinkers theoretically eat an extra 2,000 calories a month, which is equivalent to 141 ice cream cones a year, according to Lifehacker. That's quite a lot of ice cream.

Often the empty calories found in alcohol are forgotten but always add up. Enjoy special occasions guilt-free by resisting temptation and sticking to delicious mocktails, this is our top 7 fast refresh. If you haven't already, try them out now. We hope the slimmer you are, the healthier you are.

FRIDAY: DAY 26

Look, you have more friends now? That's because it makes you a really lovely person to be around, booze-free. Alcohol, as we know, allows us to lose our inhibitions, and thereby clears our minds of concentration and reason. This can lead to very offensive actions that no one wants to see.

Let your body fill with the goodness it deserves. If you need a pick-me-up, stay away from the beer and indulge in superfoods that boost your mood. We are talking about omega-rich seafood, ripe berries, and chocolate too! Healthy snacks don't have to be boring, check out the inspiration for our top 8 mood-boosting foods.

SATURDAY: DAY 27

Good news, nowadays your liver looks a lot better. Even in the short run, going alcohol-free will bring incredible benefits to your body, as discovered in a report by New Scientist. After giving up the booze for five weeks, study participants found that their liver fat dropped by up to 20 percent, reducing their risk of a massive amount of liver damage/disease. Don't you think this is a big opportunity to keep up the good work?

Why not go a step further by treating your liver with a bit of TLC? Rich antioxidant foods and beverages such as spinach, grapefruit, garlic, and green tea all contribute to a balanced, hepatic diet.

SUNDAY: DAY 28

Just guess what? You're two days out from your 30-day challenge. Just one last push and you made it thirty days sober!

If you can, avoid taking a drink to toast your achievement. Why make your booze-free trip to finish on day-30? You have come so far and done so much that it would be an utter shame to see you throw away everything. Instead of dreaming about your next boozy-weekend, focus your energy on a new mission that is more in line with the fitter, healthier you.

Check out our section on Challenge and pick one that you like. You've proven to us in the past month that you're capable of amazing stuff. Let's make it last.

MONDAY: DAY 29

You're over the hardest part, what's yet another day? Let's just take a moment to ponder what you have achieved. If you'd have (on average) a few 'regular' beers a week before, this month, you've saved around 1,500 calories for yourself. Or if your drink sessions every week were more around the seven-beer mark, you're about— 5,000 Lighter Calories.

The scales will not only be kinder, but your skin will also be smoother, your sleep, memory, and focus will increase, and you will have much more cash to spare. The 30-day challenge proves that drinking alcohol is not an integral part of your lifestyle-without it, you can relax, have fun and socialize, and that may continue.

TUESDAY: Day 30

Congratulations, Mr. President! You have completed your free 30-day booze challenge with success. It's been a month of highs and lows no doubt, but you laughed at the challenge and showed to the world what a beautifully strong person you are, well done!

How did that go for you? We'd love to hear your story booze-free…what advice would you give those just starting?

Ready to challenge you next? If you are keen to keep up the

good work and want to start on the abstinence route, click here (link to challenges) – there's plenty more to sink your teeth in.

Working in finance was stressful, numbers and meeting the bottom line were all that mattered. Everyone in the office was competing with one another to get the next client, to make the most sales, to rake in the corporate stardom and climb the ranks. I was only in my second year working for my first Venture Capitalist Company, I had long days and sleepless nights worrying about my figures for the month-end. Meanwhile my beautiful wife, Sarah, supported me from home, raising our children. My daughter Jesse was the oldest at thirteen and my son Elliot Junior (or E.J. as I liked to call him) was only eight. They were smart kids and I hope they take after their mother more than me.

One day at the office, well past 6:00pm, I was dragging, drinking my third cup of coffee for the day and knowing it would cost me sleep later. In the office next to me I could hear Jim, laughing, talking to a client on the phone and typing away at his computer. He was always like this at work, alert, on the ball, his name and praise always in the mouth of the bosses. When I heard the click of him hanging up I knocked on his door, leaning casually into the doorway. He invited me in when I knocked and closed the door behind me.

"How do you do it?" I asked him, sitting back on the back in his corner office, overlooking the cityscape. I noticed there was a bloodshot quality to his eyes but he looked wide awake and his smile unstoppable. He looked me over as if judging me for a moment before getting up, closing the blinds and sitting across from me.

"I use supplements to keep me going," he said, smirking.

"Like what...diet pills?" I had to laugh at that but he shook his head, fishing a little silver tin from his pocket.

"I powder my nose a couple times a day to keep me on the ball." I looked around wildly as he opened the small tin, white powder in little baggies filling the container. "My dealer's a client, believe it or not." He snorted a laugh and put it back in his pocket.

I blinked in disbelief, I thought that was a tale for the 80's and 90's that finance guys lived off cocaine to get them going and remain going. I had so many questions but Jim was not interested in answering them. Instead he pulled a couple of the small bags out and tossed them into my lap.

"See for yourself, you will improve like crazy," He reassured me and ushered him out of his office, mentioning a call from Overseas.

Meanwhile I had drugs on me. I had never been invited to parties in highschool and continued the trend in college on my own, focused on my studies and then I got married early and had some kids. Most I did were a couple beers after a long day to relax. I snuck into my office, already feeling like I might get caught and locked the door behind me. I shut my blinds and sat down behind my desk, settin the two baggies in front of me. I had at least three more phone calls to make and a report to write up before I could go home. My resolve going out the window I Googled how to ingest the cocaine and found numerous ways. I picked a method, felt the burn in my nose, and the drug hit my system. Hard and fast.

This is how cocaine works: it changes the chemical balance of the brain, mainly the part that controls dopamine (reward and motivation). Because of this change induced from the drug, it can alter your brain chemistry long term. Your brain gets so used from the instant large amounts of dopamine making most normal things that once triggered dopamine seem less interesting and fun. The dopamine withdrawal causes the addiction, because healthy activities no longer produce enough dopamine, your lows stay low and you are in a rut of sadness and sickness until your next hit of the drug. At first the only noticeable symptoms are feeling increased happiness, immense amounts of energy and depending on the amount you can feel out of control. As time goes and your usage and dose increases it affects your body temperature to rise, you become paranoid, your senses grow sensitive, and your stomach erodes and becomes sensitive (a lot of cocaine addicts are skinnier than the average person). Before long you begin to have constant nosebleeds, lose your smell and struggle to swallow -- mainly due to the ingestion coming from the nasal cavity. If you have too much at one you can suffer a seizure, stroke, irregular heart rhythm, or a heart attack.

You can also lose your family, like me. That is the non-science side-effect. When I had used Google for my how-to on drugs, I had ignored the bold links offering me help, warning me... All I saw was a quick fix to my current problems and for a short while, it worked. I was a star. I worked efficiently and more focused than ever, so long as about every six hours I took a hit. I started using my neighboring office as a dealer, he was elated to have a buddy in on it. My twelve hour days became eight, I was home more with my kids, I was home in time to see my beautiful wife. We had time for a date night for the first time in two years. I remember excusing myself mid-date to use the bathroom and take a hit. I also remember later that night suffering from impotence.

I did not notice it then, but my usage was heavier than Jim's and he seemed to maintain a calm demeanor more than I did. My intolerance for the drug and quick, constant usage was imbalancing my life. I took only six months for it all to be thrown away. About five months in I was showing signs of paranoia and wearing sunglasses indoors, my eyes hurting from the light. I began accusing my wife of cheating, stealing money, spying on me. I panicked when my kids knocked on the bathroom door while I was sniffing. I began to isolate myself and chose to stay at work longer, then I began to hang out with Jim, who was a divorcee and went to the bar with him. I hit on younger women to see if I could, fueled by the white stuff bumping through my veins. My impotence got worse when I tried to cheat, and was unsuccessful with a young twenty-something from the bar.

I came home to Sarah crying at the late hour, yelling at me. I brushed her off without a care to pass out on our bed. When I woke at nearly noon, the house was empty. My kids were gone and so was Sarah. A few days later I met with Sarah and she asked me what was going on, I demanded to see my kids but she refused. I did not think back then I actually wanted to see Jesse or E.J., I just wanted to be in control and I was losing my grip on life. Sarah said she and the kids were staying with her parents outside the city. I was furious, I punched the wall and yelled at her, threatened her for keeping my kids from me. She locked herself in the bathroom, called the police, and I was arrested.

She did not press charges but the incident, combined with my increasingly erratic behavior, got me fired. Jim cut me off from being my supplier from there. I did not know how to find a dealer, I went to a nightclub, feeling older and out of place but after convincing a guy I was not a cop, he became my new dealer. It was a month long bender of cocaine, loneliness, high highs and low lows. My sink was overflowing with dishes, my fridge had rotting food, and my own personal hygiene fell. All that mattered to me was another snort of the white stuff. I stopped contacting Sarah, though I tried calling the kids often, hanging up if they were not the ones answering the phone. I recall hearing my son's voice, scared and wondering when I was coming home and when I would stop being "sick." Jesse knew better than to believe the soft lie their mother had told them; whenever she answered the phone she called me names, rightfully so, and hung up on me.

It was not until there was a stranger at my door, handing me a thick stack of papers, one early morning after a bender. My eyes were bloodshot, my body aching, and heart feeling like it was in a black hole. It was my wife's lawyer, serving me with papers for a divorce. Within six months my entire life was unfolded and broken around me. I broke down and cried as I read the first page, the man standing patiently at the door. He had more than papers for me, he had advice.

"I have spoken to Sarah at length about this," he told me, while fishing for something from his pocket. "Things were rocky before, you worked long hours, but it got worse when she realized you were on something. What is it? Smack? No..." He looked me over and sighed. "Cocaine?" He frowned and produced the card he had been looking for. "My friends run a clinic, reach out, maybe if you can get your act together, you might not lose your entire family." I cried harder and took the card from him.

I dwelled on it a few days, thinking maybe I could do it on my own. I survived maybe twelve hours of cold turkey before I found remnants in a baggie I rubbed all over my gums. I had turned my home into a lecherous den of a crack house and I was its only poor occupant.

I packed a bag, wrote Sarah a letter, I left her a voicemail too to be sure he got the message. I left the keys under the doormat of the house and left to check myself into rehab. Everything was bright and clean at the facility, a large circular desk there to greet me. I felt like the filthiest thing in the room as I gripped a pen to sign in and turn in my keys, wallet, any sharp objects. They checked my clothes and bags for any drug paraphernalia, sent me to shower, they could not have things like lice or bed bugs be an issue here. Thankfully my stint had been shorter than most here and I had just layers of grime to peel off.

This was to be my first time without cocaine since I started using over six months ago. The withdrawals were terrible. My whole body ached, my muscles feeling like they had taken a beating. If I had thought I had been irritable before it was nothing compared to the agitation and restlessness I felt now without the crutch of the drug. I felt the lowest I had in ages, sometimes confused and delirious -- the anxiety I felt as intense leading to several panic attacks. I struggled with food and early mornings there, the food was healthy and the rise and shine times were earlier than I was used to. I felt fatigue as if I had been walking through a desert for days and a loss of appetite that paired well with my nausea and stomach cramps. My hollow cheeks only grew more so until I found the urge to eat once again. It took a week's worth of staying clean to stop the night sweats and shakiness. Because I was so used to my mind going a mile a minute from the dopamine, I felt bored if there was nothing to do, like creating ADD for myself. My nosebleeds had stopped to be replaced by congestion as my sinuses worked to heal like the rest of me.

Sleeping in was not a part of the program, we all got up early to have a healthy meal and attend early morning meetings. At first I shied away from the physical, dreading the idea to use my aching muscles, but after a few weeks I traded group talk for yoga and meditation. I met with a counselor and therapist to work out my issues and follow a 12-step program for my addiction and recovery. I had to face my issues, what drew me to rely on the drug, and talk about other problems. There would be a break for lunch, ability to eat it outside or indoors, under watch. They were very alert about people sneaking in drugs or alcohol, a lot of the people there were not there because they wanted to but because they were court ordered or dropped off by their parents.

I was there for three months, I had chosen their longest program of ninety days, I had family at stake and wanted to be sure I could kick this habit before I tried to get them back. I missed Sarah, E.J. and Jesse, the room I was set up in was paired with another guy, who had been on the sauce for too long, a DUI resulting in a few seriously injured bystanders had him court ordered here while his civil case was pending. He was a nice guy, a lot of regret I related to, he was younger than me though and no family. If we were in our room though we mostly slept, read, or kept to ourselves too focused on our own journeys.

When the ninety days came to an end, I was anxious, nervous I could not control myself when I was going to be back out into the world. Imagine being a man in your forties, a father, a husband, and not being able to trust yourself to be alone. I had asked Sarah to pick me up but instead it was her parents there to get me. While the proceedings for a divorce had not started, it was clear that rehab did not prove anything, I would need to prove I was better. I was

126

still fortunate that anyone had come at all to get me; I had checked myself in alone and now I was with family.

They made polite conversation and I let it remain superficial. I was informed that Sarah and the kids had moved back home and that I could go home but I would sleep in the guest room. I eagerly agreed, happy at the prospect to just see my wife and kids again. The happiness stopped there and the struggle began. I was not welcomed home with open arms but a quiet house. Sarah was in the kitchen cooking, E.J. was playing a video game, and Jesse was up in her room -- I could hear the music. As much as I wanted to hug each of them, the only one that came running was E.J. I hugged him tightly and kissed the top of his head, unable to hold back my tears. Sarah stood back, her lips pursed, she looked and torn between disappointment, disgust, and relief.

"You look better," she greeted me, keeping her distance. The last time I had seen her I had been yelling at her, threatening her, who knows if I would have ever gotten violent if it had gotten worse? I dreaded the thought and smiled at her sheepishly.

I began a slow re-introduction with my family. I set up in the guest bedroom downstairs, while my family was above me on the second floor, my wife alone in our kingsize bed, my daughter who listened to music late, and E.J. who snored. You do not realize your family is everything until you no longer have them at your side. I had missed Sarah's quick qit and laugh though her jokes had a sharper edge to them than before. I had missed E.J.'s endless curiosity, always asking questions. I had debated what I was going to tell my kids and not wanting to sugar coat it. I sat them both down to tell them what I had done, where I had been, answering any of their questions. My son had plenty, though his were more innocent, asking about the food I ate at the treatment center and asking when Sarah and I would be sleeping in the same room again.

"Your mother needs time," I told them both, ashamed of myself. "I was a terrible person. I said mean things, I behaved like an animal, things you mother does not deserve. Things you do not deserve. So until she is ready to want to be with me again, I will be in the downstairs bedroom." Sarah must have overheard because that night was the first time she hugged me and said she loved me, before retreating to our old bedroom.

Jesse did not speak to me. She often left the room if I entered it. While I made progress with my adolescent son, and even the woman I had been married to for fifteen years, I was making little headway with my teenage daughter. Sarah tried to convince me she was going through a lot, being a girl, hormones, boys, highschool... but I had a sick feeling deep in my stomach that it was not short term, that I had ruined my relationship with my daughter for the foreseeable future. I spent my time adjusting back to a new normal, getting to know my family again, or rather trying too, and making sure I did not facilitate old habits.

Sarah joined me for my morning yoga, helping us bond together again. I was elated when she let me hold her hand, sit with her on the couch, it was like rekindling our marriage all over again. I asked her out on a date and thought she might say no. We did nothing grand, the kids stayed with her parents and I attempted to cook for her. I burned it all, it tasted terrible. We ordered out and watched a movie. I got to sleep in the same bed as my wife again.

E.J. and I were on good terms the quickest, a father and son bond I was lucky to save. He helped me look for jobs, using his computer while I searched on my laptop and newspapers. While I was involved in the finance sector, my education geared towards investments and marketing I was unsure of entering that field again. The money had been good but the pressure had led me down a path I would forever regret. I rewrote my resume, and found a position at a smaller firm, less pressure on sales and more on customer service. I liked that. I even got to sell some of my three-piece suits for some quick money, as the attire was business casual for the most part. While I had been away, Sarah had started working again, returning to work as a florist, and she continued to work, enjoying the business as our kids were old enough to watch themselves at home after school. Jesse liked the freedom, or so Sarah told me, I still was on next to no communication with my little girl.

I will spend the rest of my life repairing my relationships, proving myself to them that I will never hurt them the way that I did. I was also in a constant cycle of repairing myself, and keeping myself in check. To encourage my health, my diet had changed and I no longer drank either. Exercise was a help and Sarah enjoyed joining me with it. My new job allowed me time to help E.J. with sports and I had time to see Jesse in her first high school play. Sarah's parents were still bitter, my mother in law quick to make a comment or to check in to be sure I was keeping clean. I did not object to phone searches or having drawers checked, I had a GPS locator on my phone on, ensuring accountability. I thought at first I would feel hounded, but I liked them keeping me in check, not that I felt like slipping -- I had done enough to this family.

Cocaine wiped out my life quickly, taking it all away from me in less than a year. My dependence on it had felt like an enhancement but I fell down a rabbit hole I could not escape from, where I only had the drug. I was lucky to have had life slap me in the face before it had gone on longer. I attest my recovery to my family and the addiction center, helping me get back into control. I have my health again, I have most of my family again, I hope one day to have my daughter again. I hope you will learn from my mistakes too.

CONCLUSION

There has been a lot of progress in understanding the relationship between substance abuse and family. Family influences play a significant role in understanding the emergence of drug abuse, its growth, and its progress. Treating couples and families with drug abuse issues has made positive gains. More research is needed, involving diverse and international populations. Still, effective treatments are increasing in type and number that bodes well for the improvement of millions of lives around the world.

Due to the interrelated nature of substance abuse and delinquency, the identification of substance-abusing youth in the juvenile justice system is an important first step for both their substance abuse and their delinquent behavior. Strategies for identifying drugs, followed by effective interventions, will help prevent further illicit drug use and delinquency. Drug testing can be a positive way of helping young people tackle their drug abuse denials.

Drug testing can be used as part of therapy to help young people reach and sustain rehabilitation, and to prevent certain delinquent behaviors. Successful drug recognition over time will help juvenile justice systems meet the goals of a holistic approach, including community protection, youth engagement, and the development of skills.

Addiction will ruin relationships with families, friends, and jobs. It is a chronic disease that will last for the rest of the life of the addicted person, and it is a relapsing illness. Understanding this, remaining optimistic can seem almost impossible.

But addiction can be treated, and while there is no cure, many people remain in recovery for the rest of their lives or can return after a relapse to recovery. Even though the addicted person has the potential to sustain a long and meaningful life, the chances of recovery diminish when hope fades too.

If you enjoyed this book, please let me know your thoughts by leaving a short review on Audible... Thank you

QUIT DRINKING HYPNOSIS

Learn Mindfulness And Go From Alcoholism To Sobriety -
Quit Drinking For Ever, Recover From Alcohol Addiction
And Start A New Life + 30-Day Sober Challenge

By Elliott J. Power

Did you know that can download the audiobook version of this book for free?

Thanks again for choosing this book, make sure to leave a short review on Audible if you enjoy it. I'd really love to hear your thoughts

INTRODUCTION

What is Alcoholism?

Alcoholism is the most severe type of alcohol addiction, which includes drinking habits you are unable to control. Alcohol use disorder is often generally referred to as a condition. The syndrome of alcohol use is divided into three categories: mild, moderate, and extreme. Each group has various symptoms and can cause damaging side effects. If left unchecked, alcohol addiction of any sort can escalate out of control.

Individuals who struggle with alcoholism sometimes feel that they cannot usually work without alcohol. This can contribute to a wide variety of problems; professional ambitions, personal concerns, relationships, and overall health impacts. The serious side effects of constant alcohol abuse can worsen over time and cause damaging complications.

You don't need to be secretly suffering from drug abuse. There are a lot of treatment options available to help you overcome alcohol abuse and achieve sobriety over the long term. We'll help you find the right drug recovery center to suit your needs.

"The greatest struggle in my life has been a constant sense of emptiness and being alone. Substances turned on me, and it wasn't fun or a remedy anymore. My addiction put me in dangerous situations ... I was out of control and powerless to quit.

In recuperation from alcohol dependency

Warning Drug Symptoms

There are some very clear warning signs of drug dependency. When alcohol addiction is discovered in its early stages, the probability of a successful recovery increases significantly.

Signs common to alcoholism include:

- Not being able to regulate alcohol use

- Sugar cravings when you're not drinking

- Putting alcohol above personal responsibility

- Feeling the need to continue drinking more

- Behave differently after having a drink

If you feel your alcohol intake is taking a toll on your life, it's important to find treatment options that will help you push your alcohol addiction into the background. When you are worried about your drinking, your doctor should be able to give you professional medical assistance. Sooner rather than later, finding treatment for alcoholism puts you back on track to leading a safe, satisfying life.

REASONS WHY PEOPLE DRINK

Relieve Stress

Relying on alcohol to lower the pressures of daily life may influence the probability of developing alcoholism. Since alcohol is both depressive and sedative, drinking gives rise to feelings of fun. Frequent drinking, however, creates tolerance which allows you to consume more alcohol to achieve the same effects.

Feel good

Consumption of alcohol can be a break from reality for some people. It provides a sense of relief from the underlying problems. Continuous alcohol use, however, can turn into a severe drinking addiction to get you through the day or week.

Coping with Loss

Losing a family member or friend will emotionally, physically, and mentally take a toll on you. Alcohol will relieve sadness and is used to help to get through tough times. Depending on alcohol, can spiral into a drinking problem, even temporarily.

Getting over anxiety

Many people are simply nervous, which causes them to worry about the future. Drinking reduces the inhibitions of an individual and makes them more comfortable in social situations. However, this can lead to addictive habits over time.

Lack of connection

Many people drink because they don't feel properly related to other people. We conclude that alcohol can either fill the void or maybe make forming new connections easier for them. But usually the opposite ends up being true.

Shame

Shame is one of the hardest emotions for many to cope with, and it is one of the most traumatic too. Although alcohol can temporarily mask shame with false feelings, it also causes many individuals to engage in reckless or foolish behaviors that can later make them feel even more shameful, which can lead to a downward spiral.

Trauma

Professionals in the treatment of alcoholism are seeing some form of trauma in almost every patient they treat. There are numerous forms of trauma, but they all have painful events where there was no empathetic witness for the victim. For many, the key to their recovery is the treatment of unresolved trauma.

Health Complications from Alcohol Abuse

Drinking too much can take a toll on your health – on a single occasion or over the long term. Some of the alcohol effects may have a minor effect on your health, while others may be serious or life-threatening.

Drug misuse can have short-term consequences just as harmful as long-term effects. Drinking can affect your reaction time, for example, causing you to have slow reflexes and coordination. So, it is particularly risky to drink and drive. After alcohol, getting behind a car's wheel can change your perception of speed and distance, and put yourself and others at risk.

Short-term effects of alcohol abuse may produce:

- Poor reflexes

- Slow reaction time

- Lowered inhibitions

- Reduce brain activity

- Blurry vision

- Difficulty breathing

- Restlessness

Additionally, taking too much alcohol may affect your long-term health. Some side effects can be latent for years until they start to emerge. Because of this, proper diagnosis and treatment require professional medical care.

Here are a few of the long-term health conditions caused by alcohol:

- Defaults in brain

- Wernicke-Korsakoff (neurobiological disorder) syndrome

- Liver disease

- Complications of diabetes

- Heart issues

- Increased Cancer Risk

- Brain damage

- Bone disorders

TREATMENT FOR ALCOHOLISM

Choosing to seek help with alcohol addiction is one of the biggest choices that you face. There are various types of treatment available, depending on substance dependence, prevalence, and extent. Recovering from alcohol dependence is a cycle that goes on well after treatment. It requires effort to practice and apply the strategies that you learn in recovery, counseling, support groups, and other therapy forms.

While each patient may have their recovery plan tailored to their unique needs, treatment typically follows a framework.

Treatment of alcohol addiction is divided into three sections, consisting of:

Detoxification

The first stage of recovery from alcohol abuse is detoxification. Due to the potential for severe, painful withdrawal symptoms, this process should be completed with the aid of medical professionals. Individuals are also given a drug to help ease the unpleasant side effects of withdrawal.

Rehabilitation

There are two forms of therapy used to combat alcoholism: inpatient recovery and outpatient rehabilitation. Inpatient rehabs are residential care facilities that allow you to stay for a specified period, usually 30, 60, or 90 days, in a hospital. Outpatient therapy helps patients to continue their daily lives while engaging in a recovery program. Discuss treatment options with your doctor to determine which form of recovery will best fit your needs.

Maintenance

The healing process will not stop until the treatment is done. Long-term sobriety includes regular treatment, which may include groups of support, medication, and other tools for rehabilitation. These will ensure sobriety is sustained and you can move on a safe, balanced path for months to come.

Stages of Alcoholism

As in other illnesses, there is a steady pattern of escalation in alcoholism. Drinkers who are alcohol-addicted usually go through the following phases

Pre-alcoholism - Usually, this phase is easy to miss. It is where the occasional social drink extends to several days a week to take a cocktail before dinner. This is often when people begin to grow alcohol tolerance.

Early alcoholism – This is the beginning point of alcoholism where things aren't horrible, but they may quickly become so. It is during this phase of alcoholism that people begin to have problems remembering what happens when they drink and may feel guilty for drinking.

Late Alcoholism-This is a critical alcohol period. The person loses control over what and how much he or she is drinking during this phase. This is when classical alcoholism symptoms occur, including denial, inability to participate in the workplace, fighting with family members and friends, and unsuccessful attempts to sober up. This phase of alcoholism can sometimes manifest as short abstinence followed by periods of excessive drinking.

Chronic Alcoholism – This is the last alcohol process. This stage is characterized by prolonged periods of extreme intoxication and drinking. During this period of addiction, the mental and physical health of the patient is deteriorating. This is when the person is cutting off social connections and struggling to maintain a job.

CHAPTER 1

HYPNOSIS FOR ADDICTION TREATMENT

H ypnosis is an important addiction treatment choice. Several studies have shown that you can use hypnosis, also for pathological alcoholics, as a cure for alcohol abuse in all its forms.

Hypnosis is a state of trance, essentially a modified state of consciousness-intentionally induced by a person. The change of consciousness is not something that people can imagine or experience; it is a transition that can be observed and calculated using EEG and fMRI machines.

Self-hypnosis is a type of hypnosis that involves inducing yourself into the hypnotic trance. Audio sessions on self-hypnosis lead you through a step-by-step cycle to achieve a state of altered consciousness.

What Does Hypnosis Feel Like?

You are less aware of what is going on around you when you're in a hypnotic state and more focused on some of your inner experience. This inner experience can involve thoughts, memories, emotions, or imagination.

One of the best things about the hypnotic trance is that they promote relaxation. And if you concentrate on a particular experience, subject, or feeling, you're no longer feeling anxious but more relaxed.

The Hypnotic Trance

The hypnotic trance promotes a state of relaxation. Three aspects characterize the hypnotic trance; absorption, disassociation, and suggestibility.

Absorption

Absorption may be defined as a focus of the deep mind. You get deeply absorbed and involved in your experiences when you're hypnotized, no matter what you perceive, imagine, or think about. You concentrate closely on what is going on in your head, in the same way, that you would when watching a good movie or reading a great book.

Often the visions in your head can be so vivid; you can't even say how much time has gone by since you went into the hypnotic trance.

Disassociation

Disassociation is perhaps the most important component of the drug addicts' hypnotic condition. The trance's dissociative aspect means you'll be able to separate your thoughts from other distractions.

This helps you to concentrate on one aspect, and because you are not overwhelmed by thoughts, emotions, or memories, you will

144

be able to see the experience from another viewpoint.

The value of being able to disassociate is that from a certain perspective, you can see your alcoholism. You should be able to grasp your issues, recognize the causes, and manage the feelings that will cause you to drink.

Suggestibility

You're more open to suggestions when you're in the hypnotic trance than you are in your everyday life. Don't worry, if anyone asks you to, you're not so open to suggestions as clucking like a chicken.

Irrespective of what you may have seen in movies or television shows when you are under hypnosis, you are fully in charge of your thoughts and actions. In the self-hypnosis audio session, though, the suggestions you hear guide your thoughts towards the roots of your problems.

Moreover, the suggestions offer tips on how to identify your issues and how to handle them. The hypnotic suggestions can encourage you to revisit long-forgotten memories that may shed some light on your addictive behavior or get you to think differently about your addiction.

They 're getting bigger. Since the hypnotic trance encourages relaxation and concentration, and you are open to suggestions, after all, your subconscious may decide that drinking is not good for you. Indeed, you could leave the trance with the firm belief that stopping drinking – which would normally seem difficult or almost impossible – is not only achievable but even desirable.

Hypnosis Helps You Overcome Mental Obstacles

Along with early and late alcoholism, pre-alcoholism occurs through the formation of mental barriers. Perhaps the addict chooses to drink out of habit, not because he or she needs to be intoxicated.

Most alcoholics feel guilty just by thinking of booze, let alone drinking it. Yet at the same time, without alcohol, they feel like they can't relax, sleep, or be content.

It is because, over time, alcoholics are setting up emotional hurdles for themselves. One night they cannot sleep – because we all do from time to time – because they say they can't sleep because they haven't had a drink. They feel nervous, and rather than figure out what makes them feel anxious, they drink to relax.

Perhaps worst of all, they don't feel satisfied because the drug has interfered with the release of endorphins from their brain perhaps, they drink for a better feeling.

But with the aid of hypnosis, you can overcome all those hurdles. You can remove yourself from memories or emotions while you're in a hypnotic trance and concentrate solely on your addiction. It helps you to recognize the mental barriers you have set up for yourself and prepare to overcome them.

You can surmount any challenge, no matter how high. It's all a question of motivation, and hypnosis helps a lot.

Self-hypnosis, unfortunately, has a negligible effect on untreated alcoholics. Although the hypnosis audio session helps chronic alcoholics identify and overcome their mental impediments, this category of addicts needs help in overcoming their physical addiction.

Relying on Hypnosis to Stop Drinking

The people who use hypnosis to stop drinking often come into contact with their feelings. They realize that they are strong enough to say "NO" to alcohol, and they feel capable of developing new patterns of long-term behavior that doesn't include drinking.

So, for most alcoholics, this is what it takes. When you know that while abstaining from alcohol, you can lead a normal life and you understand that your life will slowly change when you stop drinking, it is just a matter of time to achieve sobriety.

But although hypnosis is an effective treatment, it isn't magic. You'll also have to put some energy into giving up alcohol. Hypnosis enables you to understand and address your problems from a new perspective, but it depends on you and you alone quit for good.

Hypnosis helps you to consider and approach your issues from a different viewpoint, but it is up to you and you alone to quit.

Hypnosis for Alcoholism

Self-hypnosis is an effective tool for those fighting alcohol dependence. To quit drinking using hypnosis allows you to conquer your emotional problems, helping you to focus on your aims and values.

CHAPTER 2
ALCOHOLISM AND RELATIONSHIPS

The emotions and acts that create a close-knit relationship between two people are trust, contact, affection, compassion, and dedication. When these things begin to deteriorate, the relationship may begin to collapse, or may even end. An alcohol addiction mixed into any relationship can have devastating effects, particularly intimate ones.

How Does an Addiction Affect A Relationship?

When one partner is continually on an alcohol binge, it starts making a gap in the relationship's base. Much like throwing a stone at a windshield and making a crack, the strain will cause the crack to expand soon enough, and the damage will be widespread. The opposite partner may eventually not be able to see where the relationship is headed amid so much turmoil. The intimate or romantic partner is not the only one to be affected —other relationships may also be affected — children of a couple, different families, acquaintances, and even colleagues may experience harm because of the harmful effects of alcohol.

Although the one who is usually the most devastated and

negatively affected, is in many cases, the partner of the one who has the drinking problem.

This can happen for many reasons — the sober partner may now have more responsibilities to take over from the daily responsibilities of the relationship or family, including assuming greater financial obligations or childcare, in the absence of their partner. They can get tired physically and mentally as they struggle to cope with their changing lives.

When a marriage or relationship has a partner who is struggling with alcohol addiction, the other partner in the relationship is usually very unhappy. If there is a drinking problem, it also causes an immense emotional divide between the couple that tends to grow the longer the drinking persists — trust falters, resentment increases and rage then become all too prevalent. The distance can be a huge challenge in any relationship to work through. Fighting, arguing, or even violence between the two parties could begin to occur.

What Are Some Signs That an Alcohol Addiction Is Hurting A Relationship?

As explained by the American Association for Marriage and Family Therapy, when a relationship is significantly affected by alcohol abuse, there are specific warning signs that may signify a problem.

Here are a few you need to know:

- Alcohol or habits related to it appear in almost any debate, such as staying out too late or sleeping too late, avoiding important tasks or duties at home, money problems, and many more.

- The creation, on more than one occasion, of an excuse for a partner who is sick because of their alcohol intake, in an attempt to justify their behavior; examples include calling them in sick for work.

- One of the couple acknowledges that they are intoxicated to help relieve stress or discomfort associated with conflict or other interpersonal circumstances, including alcohol-related disputes.

- Drinking involves one of the primary activities that the two partners enjoy doing together.

- Violent outbursts, hostility, 'angry touching', or contempt between partners when one or both parties have had a drink.

- Whether either or both spouses need to drink to be able to interact or address the problems in the relationship freely or display signs of love or affection for the other.

- The family is getting embarrassed or feeling the need to hide from others, including other members of the family, because of someone who has an alcohol addiction.

Nonetheless, if you are aware that your relationship shows trends like these, it might be time to look at the relationship objectively, and how alcohol impacts it and finding ways to strengthen it. This may be a harsh and difficult reality to consider, and in the case of addiction, it will likely mean that the need for drinking will cease.

There's a need to look closely at the problems between the couple, including those that do not result from the drinking itself, as some problems can cause or drive a person to drink. In some cases, it may seem easier to only hope that these problems will go away, but sadly, avoiding this very real and potentially harmful problem would only help to continue to affect both individuals and relationships. The only option is to seek treatment as soon as possible, or it can spread like illness and become even more dangerous.

The Effect on Children

If a child has an alcohol-addicted parent, they are likely to undergo unpleasant and even traumatic experiences. It is especially true if they encounter such problems in the relationship between their parents. If both parents are actively involved with alcohol, a child will have a much worse experience, as opposed to when just one is. Increased rates of physical abuse, by not just one parent but two, can create for a child a very dangerous, dysfunctional home and have lasting negative impacts. It is very detrimental to witness this abuse between parents, and in some cases, the child may also experience certain forms of abuse. The latest studies show a family member afflicted with drug dependence impacts one out of four children in the United States.

What to do Next?

You're not only changing your life when you decide to seek support, but also that of those around you, such as your parents, children, or partner. As a spouse of an addicted person, it's important to give your help at this moment. Research has shown that having a partner's support when pursuing care will benefit the one who wants care to solve these problems. Getting your partner to treatment can forever change both of your lives.

It's a very common issue that the partner displaying these issues doesn't want to seek treatment or counseling or are in denial, believing they don't need help. If you are seeking help, either for yourself or a loved one, there is information, compassionate support, and a means of motivation that can help you overcome this indifference, so you can start believing in your recovery.

It's crucial to look at the emotional issues that still need to be addressed within the relationship because couples often still need help, even after the addiction is looked at and treated. Even after addressing this principal threat to the relationship, if left unchecked, a ripple effect from before can still have lasting effects on both partners. Otherwise, constant fighting could lead to more alcohol abuse, and relapse, beginning the process all over again. A long-term impact will include tackling all sides of the relationship and not just that problem. Removing alcohol from the equation is the first step, but establishing a relationship that is caring, supportive, and communicative is what will hold it stable and move forward.

There are a variety of ways to fix the issues when it comes to alcohol addiction and a relationship. Individual or community therapy and/or supportive support groups may help bring about the changes required within your relationship; however, the person who is suffering from the addiction may require a greater measure of help. The best option for a person with an alcohol addiction may be a medically assisted detox, followed by either outpatient or inpatient treatment. The good news is that many of these programs offer family therapy and support, helping families to overcome the addiction together while building a better foundation for tomorrow.

HOW ALCOHOLISM AFFECTS RELATIONSHIPS

Alcoholism does not only wreak havoc on someone's personal life, but it also has a huge effect on any single relationship they are part of. Perhaps the greatest and most damaging impacts come at the friendship, relationship, and marriage stage.

Anyone who regularly engages in heavy drinking will face many emotional, physical, and psychological challenges that tend to be expressed most fully within their closest relationships. Given their alcohol intake, people with an alcohol problem usually have a very difficult time maintaining a healthy relationship.

Alcoholism's effect on relationships and intimacy is pervasive and affects many different aspects of interpersonal relationships. This article will discuss various aspects of relationships that can be disrupted and how alcohol triggers several kinds of relationship problems.

How does alcoholism affect intimacy and sex?

The impact of alcoholism on relationships can be very negative. The first area usually affected is intimacy, which also doesn't necessarily mean sex. Parts of an intimate relationship which may be affected by the alcoholism effects include:

- Stability

- Truth

- Affection.

- Expectations.

- Respect

- Shared values.

- Commitment

It raises concern about the likelihood of codependency as well as about violent behavior when involving alcohol, both verbally and physically. Deterioration in married or unmarried couples is often the result of family disputes, financial disturbances, acts of infidelity, or, worse, violence.

Will my relationship continue with alcoholism, most people wonder? There is proof that this can be achieved through collaboration, but some can argue that it will certainly not. Research shows that this is 50 % more likely to end in divorce for the married population with one person being a heavy drinker, according to a study in Medical Daily.

How Alcohol Impacts Sex Drive

Over time, alcohol dependence would most likely result in a loss of sexual maturity in both males and females. We begin to lose interest in sex or be close to someone as their violence becomes their number one concern as a person becomes more addicted. Male alcohol misuse is known to cause difficulties in becoming or remaining aroused, often leading to erectile dysfunction. Women have also been known to suffer from reduced libido alcohol-use disorder.

Alcohol and Sexual Promiscuity

Alcohol can lead to sexually transmitted diseases or an unplanned pregnancy for people outside of a committed relationship because of having sex while under the influence of alcohol.

Evidence shows that sexual promiscuity as a consequence of alcohol is certainly something to consider for people who aren't in a serious relationship, according to a study published by Net Doctor.

How Treatment for Alcohol Abuse Can Affect A Relationship

When faced with alcoholism inside a relationship, the best choice could be to look for treatment. Treatment will help the person continue to recover from their alcohol habit and begin to lead a healthy life.

Treatment is facilitated by therapy and is accessible to all concerned parties as they try to repair their relationship. Specific therapy, as well as social or family therapy, is usually part of the substance addiction recovery plan.

Partners should pursue personal counseling with those who understand what they can feel and be a supportive group. It will help maintain stability and harmony while you support your partner through their rehabilitation.

Relationship therapy is also strongly recommended, as there are also often deeper problems that need to be discussed and handled with compassion.

CHAPTER 3
DRUG ABUSE AND ADDICTION

D o you have a drug problem or does someone that you know? Explore the warning signs and symptoms, and learn how problems with substance abuse develop.

When does drug use transform into abuse or addiction?

People can experience problems with their drug use, regardless of race, age, background, or the reason why they first started to use drugs. Some people are experimenting with recreational drugs out of curiosity, have a good time because friends do it, or relieve issues like stress, anxiety, or depression. It is not just illicit drugs like cocaine or heroin, however, that can lead to violence and addiction. Medications like painkillers, sleeping pills, and tranquilizers can cause similar problems. In reality, alongside marijuana, prescription painkillers are the most abused medications in the U.S., and more people die every day from overdosing powerful opioid painkillers than from car accidents combined with gun fatalities. As well, opioid painkiller addiction can be so strong it has become the main risk factor for heroin abuse.

Substance use — whether illicit or prescribed — does not

necessarily contribute to violence. Some people can use recreational or prescription drugs without having negative effects, while others find that substance use takes a serious toll on their well-being and health. Similarly, there is no clear point where drug use is moving from casual to problematic. Substance misuse and addiction are less about the form or quantity of the substance consumed or the duration of the use of drugs, and more about the effects of drug use. If the use of drugs creates issues in life — at work, at school, at home, or in your relationships — you are possibly having a problem with substance abuse or addiction.

If you're concerned about substance use for yourself or a loved one, learning how drug abuse and addiction develops and why it can have such a strong hold will give you a deeper understanding of how to properly cope with the problem and regain control of your life. Recognizing that you have an issue is the first step towards recovery, which involves immense bravery and energy. It can feel frightening and overwhelming to face your problem without minimizing the issue or making excuses, but recovery is within reach. Once you can seek treatment, you will conquer your addiction and create for yourself a rewarding, drug-free life.

Risk factors for drug addiction

While anybody can develop drug use problems, the vulnerability to substance addiction differs from person to person.

While anybody can develop drug use problems, the vulnerability to substance addiction differs from person to person.

While everyone may have genetic, mental health, family, and social climate issues, risk factors that increase your vulnerability include:

- Family history of dependency

- Violence, neglect or any other traumatic incidents

- Mental disorders such as depression or anxiety

- Early drug use

- Mode of administration — smoking or injecting a substance may increase the capacity for addictions

MYTHS AND FACTS ABOUT DRUG ABUSE AND ADDICTION

Here are five common myths

Myth 1: Depression is purely a matter of willpower. If you want, you can stop using the drugs.

Fact: Repeated drug use affects the brain in ways that lead to strong cravings and a compulsion to use. Those brain changes make leaving by sheer force of will incredibly difficult.

Myth 2: The use of medications such as opioid painkillers is safe because physicians prescribe them so frequently.

Fact: For example, the short-term therapeutic use of opioid pain relievers can help treat serious pain after an injury or surgery. Daily or longer-term opioid use can, however, contribute to addiction. Misuse of these medications or taking medicine from

160

someone else can be dangerous-even fatal.

Myth 3: Addiction is an illness; nothing can be done about it.

Fact: Many doctors believe that addiction is a brain-influenced disorder, but that doesn't mean everyone is powerless. The addiction-related brain changes can be treated and reversed through therapy, medication, exercise, and other treatments.

Myth 4: Addicts must reach the rock bottom before they can progress.

Fact: At any point in the addiction process, rehabilitation will begin — and the sooner, the better. The longer the misuse of drugs occurs, the greater the addiction is, and the harder it becomes to handle. Don't wait until the abuser has nothing to lose.

Myth 5: You can't push someone into treatment; they need to seek help.

Fact: To be successful, the treatment doesn't have to be voluntary. People who are under pressure from their family, employer, or the legal system to receive treatment are just as likely to benefit as those who choose to receive treatment alone. When they sober up and clear their head, many previously stubborn addicts realize they want to improve.

Myth 6: Previously, therapy didn't succeed, so there's no point trying again.

Fact: Drug addiction recovery is a lengthy process, often

involving setbacks. Relapse does not mean treatment fails or sobriety is a lost cause. Instead, it's a warning to get back on track by either going back to rehab or changing the approach to treatment.

HOW DRUG ABUSE AND ADDICTION DEVELOPS

There is a fine line between daily substance use and addiction and substance misuse. Very few substance abusers or addicts may know this line after they have crossed it. Although the amount or quantity of drugs consumed may not automatically constitute substance abuse or addiction, they may also be signs of substance-related issues.

Suppose the drug fulfills a valuable need. You may find that you depend more and more on it. You can take illegal drugs to calm down or energize or make you more comfortable. You may begin to misuse prescription medications to alleviate pain, cope with panic attacks, or boost school or work focus. You are more at risk of crossing the line from recreational drug use to substance misuse and addiction if you are using drugs to fill a gap in your life. You need to feel good and have positive experiences in your life without any drug use to maintain a healthy balance in your life.

Drug abuse may start as a way to socially connect. Users also try drugs with friends and colleagues for the first time in social settings. A strong urge to fit into the community can make it feel as though the only choice is to do the drugs with them.

Often issues will creep up on you, as the drug use grows

162

slowly over time. Smoking a weekend joint with friends, or taking ecstasy at a rave, or painkillers when your back aches, for example, may change from using drugs a few days a week to using them daily. Gradually it is more and more important for you to get and use the medication.

When substance addiction takes root, for work or school, you may miss or always be late, your job performance may slowly deteriorate. You may start neglecting social or family obligations. The capacity to stop using inevitably ends up being affected. What began as a voluntary option has become a physical and psychological need.

Drug addiction will ultimately overtake your life, slowing social and academic progress. This only increases feelings of loneliness.

DRUG ADDICTION AND THE BRAIN

Although each drug causes various physical effects, one thing all abused drugs have in common is that prolonged use can affect the way the brain works. This includes medicines that are commonly abused as well as recreational drugs.

• Taking this medicine causes a rush of the hormone dopamine in your brain that triggers pleasure. Your brain recalls these feelings and wants to repeat them.

• The drug acquires the same meaning as you become addicted to other coping habits, such as eating and drinking.

• Brain changes interfere with your ability to think, exercise sound judgment, monitor your actions, and feel safe without drugs.

• Whatever substance you are addicted to, the uncontrollable compulsion to use is more vital than everything else, including your family, friends, job, and even your wellbeing and happiness.

• The desire to do it is so intense that your mind seeks multiple ways to deny addiction or to rationalize it. You can underestimate dramatically the quantity of drugs you are taking, how much it affects your life, and how much control you have over your drug use.

You can overcome the harmful effects of substance use with the right treatment and help, and regain control of your life. The first challenge is acknowledging and accepting that you have a problem or listening to loved ones who are always more able to see the negative impact that substance use has on your life.

Symptoms and signs of drug abuse and addiction

The signs of addiction are identical although different medications have different physical effects. If you identify in yourself the following signs and symptoms of substance abuse and addiction, address your drug use with others.

Common signs and symptoms of drug abuse

Neglecting responsibilities at home, work, or school (e.g. skipping work, flunking classes neglecting your children).

Taking drugs in unsafe environments, or taking high risks,

such as using dirty needles, driving on drugs, or having sex without protection.

I am experiencing legal trouble, such as convictions for disorderly conduct, driving under the influence, or stealing to sustain a drug habit.

Problems in your relationships, such as disputes with your wife or family members, an unhappy boss, or the loss of friends.

Common Signs of Drug Addiction and Its Symptoms

You have built up a tolerance to drugs. You need to use more of the medication to feel the same effects than with the smaller doses that you used to take.

You use them to avoid or alleviate symptoms of withdrawal. You will experience symptoms such as nausea, restlessness, insomnia, fatigue, sweating, trembling, and anxiety if you go too long without medication.

Loss of control over their use of drugs. You still do drugs or use more than you have expected, even though you said you would not. You might want to stop using it, but you're feeling powerless.

Their lives revolve around the use of drugs. You spend a lot of time thinking about and using drugs, figuring out how to get them, or recovering from the effects of the drug.

Because of your drug use, you have abandoned activities you used to enjoy, such as hobbies, sports, and socializing.

You continue to use drugs, although you know it hurts you.

It's triggering big life problems — blackouts, financial issues, illnesses, mood swings, insomnia, paranoia — but you're still using it anyway.

Signs That A Friend or Relative Is Abusing Drugs

Drug abusers sometimes seek to hide their symptoms and downplay their problems. If you're worried that a friend or relative may misuse drugs, check out the following warning signs:

- Psychological alarm signals

- Bloodshot eyes, bigger pupils or smaller than normal

- Changes in the level of appetite or amount of sleep

- Breakdown or weight gain

- Deteriorating body appearance, personal grooming habits

- Unusual breath, body, or clothing odors

- Tremors, slurred speech, or coordination impairment

Behavioral warning signs

- Fall in attendance either at work or school

- Unreported financial problems; borrowing or theft

- Engage in illegal or questionable activity

- Sudden change in friends, hobbies and favorite hangouts

- Getting into trouble frequently (fights, accidents, illegal activities)

Psychological warning signs

- Unclear personality change or attitude change

- Unexpected mood swings, irritability or outbursts of frustration

- Periods of unusual hyperactivity, restlessness or giddiness

- Motivation deficiency; looks lethargic or "spaced out"

- Looks scared, nervous or paranoid

Warning signs of commonly abused drugs

Marijuana: Glassy, red eyes; loud talking, unsuitable laughter followed by sleepiness; loss of interest, motivation; weight gain, or loss.

Stimulants (including amphetamines, cocaine, crystal meth): dilated pupils; hyperactivity; euphoria; irritability; anxiety; rapid speech accompanied by depression or irregular sleep; can go on for long periods without eating or sleeping; loss of weight; dry mouth and nose.

Inhalants (glues, aerosols, vapors): watery eyes; impaired vision, memory, and thinking; nose secretions or rashes around the nose and mouth; headaches and nausea; pallid appearance; drowsiness; poor muscle control; appetite changes; anxiety; irritability; lots of cans/aerosols in the trash.

Hallucinogens (LSD, PCP): dilated pupils; bizarre, irrational behavior including paranoia, aggression, hallucinations; mood swings; detachment from humans; self-absorption or other objects; slurred speech; confusion.

Heroin: contracted pupils; no pupils' reaction to light; needle tracks; sleeping at odd times; sweating; vomiting; coughing, sniffing; twitching; lack of appetite.

Warning signs of prescription drug abuse and addiction

Prescription drug abuse has become an escalating problem in recent years, most commonly involving opioid painkillers, anti-anxiety drugs, sedatives, and stimulants. Many people start taking these medicines to cope with a specific medical problem — taking painkillers, for example, after an injury or surgery. Nevertheless, increased doses are required over time to maintain the same pain relief level, and some patients may become physically dependent, experiencing signs of withdrawal if they attempt to stop taking the drug. One of the early warning signs of a developing problem is that the effect of the drug wears off at a faster than normal pace. In other cases, people begin to abuse unprescribed medication to experience a high, relieve tension, increase alertness, or improve concentration.

To avoid problems with prescription medication, it is important that you only take it as directed, use the lowest dose for the shortest possible period and talk to your doctor about other methods of treating the problem. Being conscious of the symptoms of dependence can help to detect issues with prescription drugs at an early stage and help avoid their development into addiction.

Warning signs of commonly abused prescription drugs

Opioid painkillers (including OxyContin, Vicodin, Norco): drooping eyes, constricted pupils even in dim light, extreme itching or flushing, slurred speech; drowsiness, loss of energy; inability to focus, lack of motivation, the decline in work or school performance; neglect of friendships and social activities;

Anti-anxiety drugs, sedatives, and hypnotics (including Xanax, Valium, Ambien): constricted pupils; drunk, slurred speech, concentration difficulty, clumsiness; poor judgment, drowsiness, slow breathing.

Stimulants (including Ritalin, Concerta, Adderall, and Dexedrine): dilated pupils, decreased appetite; agitation, anxiety, irregular heartbeat, high body temperature; insomnia, paranoia.

If you think a friend or member of your family has a drug addiction, here are a few things you can do:

Talk about it. Talk about your concerns to the individual, and give your help and support without being judgmental. Early addiction treatment is more successful. You should not wait before one of your loved ones reaches the edge! List specific examples of the behavior of your loved ones that worry you and urge them to seek assistance.

Pay heed to yourself. Don't get caught up so much in the drug problem with someone else that you neglect your own needs. Make sure you have people that you can talk to and lean on to help.

Avoid blaming yourself. You should help a person with a problem with substance abuse and promote recovery, but you cannot compel a drug abuser to change. You can't control the decisions that your loved one makes. Letting the person take responsibility for their actions is an important step along the path to recovery.

Don't...

- Try threatening, punishing, bribery, or preaching.

- Make emotional arguments that simply attach shame to the user's emotions and enhance the desire to use drugs.

Cover up or make excuses for the drug abuser or shield them from the consequences of their drug use.

- Take over the responsibilities of the drug abuser and decrease their sense of self-worth.

- Hide drugs or throw them away.

- If they're high, argue with the person.

- Use drugs with individuals.

- Feel guilty or responsible for the behavior of a drug-abuser.

If your teen's having a drug problem

Discovering that your child uses drugs can cause anxiety, uncertainty, and frustration. When confronting your teen, it's important to remain calm and to do so only when everyone is sober. Explain your worries and make it clear that a place of love

170

is your concern. It's important that you feel supportive of your teen.

Warning signs of drug abuse among teens

Like adults, abuse of drugs by adolescents is not limited to illegal drugs. Teens are more likely to misuse prescription and over-the-counter drugs, including painkillers, stimulants, sedatives, and tranquilizers. Such medications are in many cases much easier for teenagers to procure, but they can have dangerous side effects, including lethal ones.

While experimenting with any type of drug doesn't automatically lead to drug abuse, early use is a risk factor in developing more serious drug abuse and addiction in the future. The risk of substance addiction often significantly increases during transitional periods, such as changing colleges, moving, or divorce. The challenge for parents is to differentiate between the normal, often volatile, teen-year ups and downs and the red flags of substance abuse. Including:

- **Having bloodshot eyes or dilated pupils**; trying to conceal these symptoms with eye drops

- **Skipping class**; falling grades; getting into trouble at school unexpectedly

- **A lack of prescriptions, medicines, money or valuables**

- **Acting lonely, withdrawn,** angry or distressed uncharacteristically

- **Sudden changes in mood** or frequent health problems,

chronic tiredness

- **Drop one group of friends for another**: be secretive about the new group of peers

- **Loss of interest in old hobbies**; new passions and new practices

- **To seek more privacy**; to lock doors; to avoid eye contact; to sneak around

7 Steps Parents Can Take to Curb Teen Drug Use

1. **Speak frankly with your children about the risks of both illicit and prescription drug use.** Providing a secure and open place to address these things will make a huge difference in the probability they may be using or abusing drugs.

2. **Set the laws and the implications.** Your teen should understand that drug use has certain consequences. But don't make hollow threats or set rules you can't enforce — and make sure your spouse agrees and is willing to enforce the rules. Remind your teen that it's illegal to take a prescription from someone else or share theirs with others.

3. **Monitor activity in your teen.** Know where your teen 's going and who they're hanging out with. It is also important to check on a routine basis potential drug hiding places — in backpacks, between books on a shelf, in cases of DVDs or makeup cases. To search for unauthorized online

transactions, track your teen's use of the Internet.

4. **Hold medications on prescription in a safe spot**, stop keeping them, and dispose of any unused prescription medicines. Carefully track your drug re-fills.

5. **Encourage other desires and practices within society**. Reveal healthy hobbies and activities to your teens, such as team sports and after-school clubs.

6. **Talk with your child about the underlying problems**. Other problems can result from drug use. Is it difficult for your teen to fit in? Has there been a major change recent like a stress-causing move or divorce?

7. **Here's help**. Teenagers frequently protest against their parents but may be more likely to listen if they hear the same details from a different authority figure. Seek a fitness psychologist, family doctor, addiction counselor, or therapist.

Next step: Get help for

Abuse or Addiction Assistance

Addiction is a complex issue that touches every aspect of your life. Overcoming addiction involves reaching out for help and making improvements to the way of life, coping with issues, and being connected to others. It's very easy to get depressed and rationalize "just one more." Whether you want to go to recovery, rely on self-help services, get counseling, or take a self-directed treatment strategy, encouragement is important.

CHAPTER 4

WHY IS IT SO HARD TO QUIT DRINKING?

Alcoholism is an addiction that affects the behavior and conduct of an individual. It's a disease that doesn't happen overnight, and it's not something that somebody chooses in the same way they don't choose to have flu, stroke, or heart attack. Dependence on alcohol needs medication as much as other diseases do. The risk of relapse is still present, and the person with the addiction will work hard to maintain his or her sobriety.

It's not easy to stop drinking after you've been addicted, but it can be achieved with the proper care and help. The toughest thing for some, however, is simply admitting that there is a problem first.

Admitting the Problem Exists

Not realizing that they have a serious addiction is a common feature among addicts. Many with alcoholism realize they want a drink but still wouldn't believe they need to drink. They also feel they can stop drinking at any moment and tell loved ones they can stop if they wish.

Others may know their drinking has become a problem but are afraid to give up. They may have tried sometime before going without a drink but found it very tough. They may face comments from loved ones saying they should 'just stop'. Nevertheless, there would be no addicts in the world if it were that easy just to stop. Those with no addiction experience often think it is simply a case of quitting, and that is the end of the problem. Nonetheless, those affected by addiction know this couldn't be any further from reality.

Most addicts find it easier to convince someone they don't have a problem than trying to quit. It's easier to blame others for drinking or find excuses as to why they can't quit right now. Those who continue to drink will, however, harm their relationships and health.

DANGERS OF ALCOHOLISM

There are numerous reasons to avoid drinking, and the reasons for keeping drinking are far outweighed. Alcohol is a chemical substance, and there's no safe limit to alcohol consumption in terms of the risk of certain diseases developing.

Nevertheless, people who drink more than the recommended daily alcohol limits are at risk of developing alcohol-related health problems including liver disease, high blood pressure, and neck, throat, and mouth cancers.

Alcoholism can cause irregular sleeping patterns, sex life issues, and the likelihood of injury in an accident may increase.

Fear of Recovery

If you're an alcoholic, the fear of being rehabilitated may keep you off getting help. During the past, you may have found it hard to quit and may have heard tales of how painful symptoms of withdrawal are.

The reality is that giving up alcohol is difficult, but it is not impossible. Your body has become alcohol-dependent and will crave it once it does not get it anymore. There are—however, several excellent rehab facilities in the country, providing healthy detoxification. You will be medically treated at these facilities, and medicine will be given to relieve the symptoms.

Feeling afraid of the unknown is normal, but what is the worst that might happen? You may suffer any adverse side effects, but you may have the chance to live without addiction for the rest of your life. If you just want to become sober, then now is the time to make the transition and to commit to a recovery lifestyle. Today, contact an addiction helper for advice and support to take the next step.

Two Big Myths About Quitting Drinking

Numerous people have been addicted ever since humans found out how to make alcoholic beverages. Unfortunately, when society began to tackle the problem, our common understanding of alcoholism became rooted in many false ideas.

#1: Quitting Drinking Is All About Willpower

There's a perception out there that you'd be able to stop drinking if you just "had more self-control" In fact, the long-term and regular consumption of alcohol changes the brain chemistry, so you become physically dependent on it — you need alcohol to feel normal. That's why our scientifically validated alcohol recovery plan is effective — we are working with FDA-approved medications and clinically proven supplements, personalized to your individual needs, to get your brain chemistry back to normal.

#2: Only A Higher Power Can End Your Drinking

We 're not attacking anybody's set of beliefs. Miracles happen, and faith is important to so many of us. Keep an open mind.

The problem is we have developed drug recovery programs that are predicated on not being responsible for their actions by the patient. The abuse has also been transformed into a belief that alcoholism is a moral failure.

Faith can play an important role in recovery, but science has shown that medication can be used to treat the core problem of altered brain chemistry. Believe that you can feel good again with behavioral changes, without having alcohol.

CHAPTER 5
DIFFERENCE BETWEEN ABUSE AND
ADDICTION

What is the distinction between, and are they related, substance addiction and drug dependence? It's a difficult problem, and it may not always be easy to say when someone you care for crosses the line from a substance dependency into a full-blown addiction.

The difference is in the number of diagnostic criteria according to the Mental Disorders Diagnostic and Statistical Manual (DSM), as published by the American Psychiatric Association and used by physicians and the court system alike.

However, when it comes down to it, no matter what the specifics, the effects of chronic drug use and addiction can damage every aspect of a person 's life, and if moderation of that use alone is impossible, then treatment can help.

Drug Abuse

Problems of persistent drug misuse are often viewed as less harmful than drug addiction, but the fact is that the continued use of illegal drugs can be just as detrimental to the life of the user. Therefore, treatment services are available to those who are struggling with either issue.

Drug misuse is described by one or more of the following problems over the past year:

- Legal issues caused by substance misuse or affected behaviors

- Physical harm to others caused by the use of drugs by an individual and/or his behaviors under the influence (or lack of action due to drug use);

- Inability to do what is required at home, at school, at work or in general to handle responsibilities

- Continuing use of drugs in these and other areas, despite ongoing issues caused by substance misuse

Drug Addiction

If you encounter three or more of the following problems during 12 months, you can meet the requirements for an addiction diagnosis:

- The onset of symptoms of withdrawal (physical and psychological) if without the drug of choice

- Use of greater and greater amounts of the product of choice to produce the same initially observed results

- Less interest in old interests, or career/school activities

- Removal from family and friends

- Behavioral changes that revolve solely around getting or keeping high

- Several attempts to reduce or stop drug use without success

- Continued use of drugs and alcohol despite the continuing and increasing problems.

The Connection

Addiction will not take off immediately. It takes time to build up a tolerance to the drug of choice, develop drug cravings, and experience problems with illicit substance use. Drug abuse usually occurs first. While it may sound like an addiction at its worst, there is one main aspect that makes opioid dependency special.

The first sign is the inability to halt drug and alcohol use. Someone who is dealing with substance abuse may have a variety of issues that affect people with addiction, but he may be able to avoid using all drugs without a problem for a long time. An abuser, despite a keen desire to quit using, cannot stay away from his drug of choice and/or other substances.

Continuing drug or alcohol addiction can lead to dependency. Regular use creates a tolerance that, when without the drug can, in turn, mean the experience of withdrawal symptoms. Similarly, ongoing drug use, especially for a specific purpose such as relaxing, dealing with anger, or managing other emotions or mental health symptoms that are problematic, can create the belief that drug use is necessary to function, thus creating psychological dependence.

CHAPTER 6
OVERCOMING ALCOHOL ADDICTION

A re you willing to quit drinking or cut to healthier levels? These tips may help you get off the road to recovery.

How can I stop taking a drink?

Overcoming an alcohol addiction can be a bumpy and long path. It can even feel impossible at times. But this is not so. When you're able to stop drinking and get the treatment you need, you will recover from substance abuse — no matter how heavy your drinking is, or how helpless you feel. And you don't have to wait until you reach the rock bottom, at any moment you can make a shift. These guidelines can help you get started on the road to recovery today, whether you want to quit drinking altogether or cut down to healthier levels.

Most people with problems with alcohol do not choose to make a big change out of the blue or transform their drinking habits overnight. Recovery tends to be a more gradual process. Denial is a huge impediment in the early stages of change. You may also make excuses after admitting that you have a drinking problem, and drag your feet. Recognizing your ambivalence about stopping drinking is critical. When you're not sure whether you're ready to adjust or are struggling with the decision, it will help you think about each choice's costs and benefits.

Evaluating the Costs and Benefits of Drinking

Make a table like the one below, weighing drinking costs and benefits against the cost and benefits of quitting.

Is drinking worth the cost?

Benefits of drinking

- Allows me to forget my issues.

- I'm having fun when drinking.

- After a hard day, it is my chance to relax and unwind.

Benefits of NOT drinking

- I am potentially strengthening my relationships.

- I will be feeling emotionally and physically healthier.

- I will have more time and energy for the people I care for and for the activities.

Costs of drinking

- This created issues with my relationships.

- I feel sad, nervous, and embarrassed.

- My job success and family commitments get in the way.

Costs of NOT drinking

- I will have to find a better way to tackle the issues.

- I would be losing my drinking buddies.

- I 'd have to face up to the obligations I neglected.

Set Goals and Prepare for Change

The next move, after you've made the decision to alter, is to set specific drinking goals—the more precise, the more practical, and the simpler the goals, the better.

Example # 1: My target for drink

- I am not drinking alcohol

- My quit date is _____ .

Example #2: My drinking goal

- On weekdays I should quit drinking, starting as of

- I'll limit my drinking on Saturday and Sunday to no more than three drinks a day, or five drinks a weekend.

- Three months later, I'll cut back on my weekend drinking even more than two drinks a day and three drinks a weekend.

Want to stop drinking or just cut down altogether? Decide which days you will drink alcohol and how many drinks you will allow yourself per day if your goal is to reduce your drinking. Consider committing to not drinking at least two days per week.

When would you like to stop drinking, or drink

less? Someday? In one week? Next month, then? In just six months? Set a specific quit date if you're trying to stop the drinking.

How to meet your goals

Once you have set your goals of either quitting or cutting down on your drinking, write down some suggestions about how to help you meet those goals. For instance:

Get rid of those temptations. Remove from your home and workplace all beer, barware, and other paraphernalia associated with beer.

Advertise your goal. Let friends, family members, and coworkers think you're trying to avoid drinking or cut back. If they drink, remind them not to do so in front of you, to help your recovery.

Be upfront about your new boundaries. Make it clear that you will not be allowed to drink in your home, and that you may not be able to attend alcohol serving events.

Stop such negative influences. Distance yourself from people who do not endorse your attempts to avoid drinking or to follow the boundaries that you have set. It may mean giving up some friends and some social connections.

Know from experience. Focus on previous efforts to avoid or cut down on your drink. What went wrong? What didn't happen? How do you prevent mistakes better this time?

Cutting Back Vs. Quitting Alcohol Altogether

The extent of your alcohol addiction depends on whether or not you can effectively cut back on your alcohol. If you're an alcoholic — which means you can't regulate your drinking by definition — it's best to try and quit drinking altogether. But if you are not prepared to take that step, or if you have no problem with alcohol abuse but want to cut back for personal or health reasons, the following tips may help.

Set your goal of drinking. Pick a cap on how much you're going to drink, but make sure your cap isn't more than one drink a day if you're a woman, two drinks a day if you're a man — and aim to have a few days a week when you're not going to consume any alcohol. Write down your drinking target and put it where you can always see it, e.g. on your phone or taped to your fridge.

Keep your drinking history of helping you achieve your goal. Write down any time you have a drink for 3 to 4 weeks, and how much you drink. Reviewing the results of your weekly drinking habits might surprise you.

Cut back on home drinking. Try to limit or remove your alcohol from home. Avoiding drinking is much easier if you don't keep the temptations around.

Drink lighter. Drink slowly, and have a 30-minute or one-hour break between drinks. Instead of alcoholic beverages, drink soda, water, and tea. It's never a good idea to drink on an empty stomach, so make sure you eat food before you drink.

Schedule one or two days off alcohol per week. Then, try a week with days off drinking. Take note about how you feel on these days physically and mentally — recognizing the benefits may help you cut back for good.

Alcohol Addiction Treatment Options

Some people can stop drinking alone or with the help of a 12-step program or another support group, while others need medical supervision to safely and comfortably withdraw from the alcohol. Which option is best for you depends on how much you have been drinking, how long you have had a problem, how stable your living situation is, and what other health issues you may have?

Examples of alcohol treatment programs

Residential treatment involves living in a treatment facility during the day while undergoing intensive treatment. The residential care typically lasts from 30-90 days.

Partial hospitalization is for individuals who require continuous medical monitoring. These treatment programs usually meet 3-5 days a week at the hospital, 4-6 hours a day.

Intensive outpatient programs (IOPs) are focused on prevention of relapse, and can often be planned around work or school.

Therapy (individual, group, or family) will help you recognize the root causes of your alcohol use, fix your relationships, and learn new coping strategies.

Tips on how to better treat addictions

There is no magic bullet or single treatment that works for everyone. The needs of everybody are different, so it is important to find a program that feels right for you. Any recovery plan for alcohol abuse should be personalized to suit your particular circumstances and needs.

Treatment should not be confined to physicians and psychologists. Many clergy, social workers, and psychologists also have resources for treating addiction.

Treatment should address more than just your alcohol abuse. Addiction affects your whole life, including your relationships, career, health, and psychological well-being. The success of treatment depends on understanding how alcohol abuse has influenced you and creating a new way of life.

Commitment and follow-through are key. Recovering from alcohol addiction or heavy drinking is not a quick and easy process. Typically speaking, the longer and more frequent the alcohol intake, the longer and more extensive the care you will require. But irrespective of the duration of weeks or months of the treatment plan, long-term follow-up care is vital to the rehabilitation.

Have other medical or mental health problems handled? People also use alcohol to relieve the effects of an undiagnosed issue of mental health, such as depression or anxiety; When you are seeking help with alcohol abuse, it is also important that you receive care for any other psychological problems that you are experiencing. Your best hope of success is to get mental health and alcohol care combined from the same treatment provider or team.

Withdrawing from alcohol safely

Your body becomes physically dependent on alcohol when you drink heavily and frequently and goes through withdrawal if you suddenly stop drinking. Alcohol withdrawal symptoms vary from mild to severe, and include:

- Shaking

- Sweating

- Headache

- Anxiety and restlessness

- Nausea or vomiting

- Stomach cramps and diarrhea

- Trouble sleeping or concentrating

- Elevated heart rate and blood pressure

Alcohol withdrawal symptoms usually start within hours after you stop drinking, peak in a day or two, and improve within five days. But in some alcoholics, withdrawal is not just unpleasant —

it can be life-threatening.

If you are a long-term, heavy drinker, you can need to be detoxified with medical supervision. A detox may be performed as an out-patient, or in a hospital or drug rehab center, where medication may be administered to avoid medical problems and alleviate symptoms of withdrawal. To know more, consult with your doctor or recovery counselor.

Seek emergency medical help if you experience any of the following withdrawal symptoms:

- fever

- confusion and disorientation

- severe vomiting

- hallucinations

- seizures or convulsions

- extreme agitation

The above symptoms may be a sign of a severe form of alcohol withdrawal called delirium tremens, or DTs. This unusual, emergency disorder triggers dangerous changes in how your brain controls your blood and breathing, so getting to the hospital quickly is critical.

Get support

Help is important when you want to combat your alcohol problem by going through counseling, undergoing therapy, or taking a self-directed treatment strategy. Don't just try to do it alone.

It's much easier to recover from alcohol addiction or abuse when you have people that you can count on for encouragement, comfort, and guidance.

Support can come from family members, counselors, friends, other alcoholics who are healing, your health care providers, and people from your community.

Lean on close friends and family – A valuable asset in recovery is having the support of friends and family members. When you are reluctant to turn to your loved ones because you have let them down before, consider seeking counseling or family therapy for couples.

Develop a sober social network – You might need to make some new connections if your previous social life revolved around alcohol. Sober friends are valuable to have and who will help your recovery. Attempt to take a class, join a church or a civic organization, volunteer, or attend community events.

Consider meetings a priority-join a support group on recovery and attend daily meetings. It can be healing to spend time with people who understand exactly what you're going through. You will also take advantage of the group members' common experiences and hear what others have done to remain sober.

Find New Meaning in Life

While getting sober is a significant first step, your recovery from alcohol abuse or heavy drinking is just the beginning. Rehab or medical counseling will get you on the road to recovery, but to remain alcohol-free for the long term, you will need to create a healthy, fulfilling life in which drinking has no place anymore.

Five steps to a sober lifestyle

1. **You are caring about yourself.** Concentrate on eating well and having plenty of sleep to avoid mood swings and battle the cravings. Exercising is also important: it releases endorphins, relieves stress, and promotes emotional well-being.

2. **Build your network for support.** Surround yourself with people who make you feel good. The more you invest in yourself and your life, the more you gain— which will help you stay motivated and on the road to recovery.

3. **Create new projects and interests.** Find new hobbies, volunteering activities, or work that will give you a sense of purpose and meaning. You'll feel better about yourself when you're doing things that you find rewarding and alcohol will have less appeal.

4. **Keep on medication.** Whether you engage in a community group such as Alcoholics Anonymous, have a mentor, or are interested in counseling or an outpatient recovery clinic,

your chances of staying sober increase.

5. **DEAL with stress in a balanced manner**. Drug misuse is also a futile attempt at stress reduction. Find healthier ways to control your stress levels, such as exercising, meditating, breathing exercises, or other relaxation techniques.

Plan for Triggers and Cravings

Alcohol cravings can be intense, especially in the first six months after you have stopped drinking. Good drug treatment will prepare you for these problems, allowing you to build new coping mechanisms to cope with stressful circumstances, drug cravings, and social drinking pressure.

Avoiding Drinking Triggers

Ignore stuff that will cause the desire to drink. If certain people, places, or activities trigger an alcohol craving, try avoiding them. It can involve making significant changes to your social life, such as finding new things to do with your old drinking buddies — or even leaving those friends and finding new ones.

In social settings, practice saying "no" to the alcohol. If you're trying to stop alcohol, there'll still be moments when you're given a beer. Prepare for how you'll react, "no thanks," with a firm but polite answer.

Manage Alcohol Cravings

Try these approaches when you are dealing with alcohol

cravings:

Talk to someone you trust: your sponsor, a supportive member or friend of your family or someone from your community of faith.

Distract yourself before the impulse gets in. Go for a stroll, listen to music, do some home cleaning, run an errand, or do a short job.

Remind yourself about why you don't drink. There's a tendency to consider the positive aspects of drinking when you want alcohol and forget the negative ones. Consider the long-term adverse effects of heavy drinking, and how it does not always make you feel better, even in the short run.

Consider the impulse, and ride it out, rather than battling it. It is known as "urge surfing." Think of your desire as a wave hitting the beach that will soon crash, crack and dissipate. When you ride out the craving, without attempting to fight, judge, or ignore it, you will see that it passes faster than you would think.

The three basic steps of urge surfing:

1. **Evaluate how you experience your craving**. Sit in a comfortable chair with your feet down, on the floor and relaxed posture with your legs. Take a few deep breaths, and concentrate. Let your mind wander around your body. Note the part of your body where you feel the cravings and what the feelings are like. Just tell yourself how it feels. "My appetite is in my mouth and

nose, and my stomach, for starters."

2. **Focus on one place where the desire is felt.** How do the sensations feel in that area? Perhaps you feel cold, hot, tingly, or numb, for example? Do you have tight or relaxed muscles? How much is one region involved? Describe to yourself the feelings, and any changes that can occur. "My mouth feels parched and hot. My lips and tongue are tense. I'm still sweating. I can picture the smell and tingle of a drink as I exhale.

3. **Repeat on every part of your body that feels the craving.** What changes do the sensations make? Notice how and when the urge comes. You'll probably notice that the craving went away after a few minutes. The urge to surf is not to make cravings go away, but to experience them in a new way. You'll learn how to ride the cravings out with practice before they eventually go away.

Handling Setbacks in Your Recovery

Recovery of alcohol is a process, one that sometimes includes setbacks. Don't give up when you fall or relapse. A drinking relapse does not mean you're a loser, or you're never going to be able to achieve your goal. Every drinking relapse is an opportunity to learn and commit to sobriety, so in the future, you will be less likely to recur.

What to do if you slip:

- Get rid of the alcohol and get away from where you've had a relapse

- Note, one drink or a brief pause should not turn into a full-blown relapse

- Don't use feelings of remorse or shame to put you back on track

- Immediately contact your mentor, counselor or helpful friend for help

How to Help Someone Stop Drinking

Abuse of alcohol and addiction not only affects the intoxicated person — but it also affects their families and loved ones. It can be as heartbreakingly traumatic and upsetting to watch a family member suffer from a drinking addiction. But while you cannot do the hard work of overcoming your loved one's addiction, your love, and support that play a crucial role in their long-term recovery.

Discuss their drinking with the person. Communicate your thoughts carefully, and invite support from your friend or family member. Seek to remain calm and don't complain, yell, accuse, or attack.

Check for addiction advice in anything you can. Investigate the forms of care available, and explore these choices with your friend or family member.

Take action. Try setting up a family meeting or intervention, but don't put yourself in a position of risk. Provide help on every step of the recovery process.

Don't make excuses for your loved one's behavior. The person who has the drinking problem has to take responsibility for their acts.

Let the blame be on yourself. You're not to blame your loved one for the drug crisis because you can't make them healthier.

CHAPTER 7

CAUSES OF ALCOHOLISM AND RISK FACTORS

Alcoholism is a disease that does not discriminate and can affect anyone irrespective of age, gender, ethnicity, body shape, or personal beliefs.

There are certain causes and risk factors for alcoholism?

Numerous studies have focused on the causes and risk factors associated with alcoholism over the past few decades. Although there is no precise mechanism for portraying a person's drinking behaviors, data have shown that several variables affect substance misuse. Alcoholism, however, is a disorder that does not discriminate and can affect anyone irrespective of age, gender, race, body shape, or personal beliefs.

Alcohol dependence may develop rapidly and violently, or it can emerge over a longer period. No matter where or how a drinking addiction begins, there are plenty of recovery options available to help you get back on track with your life. Seeking medical treatment will give you the best chance of lifelong sobriety.

If you or a loved one are struggling with an alcohol-use

disorder, help is just a call away from you. Call a care provider now to find out what recovery services are available and to locate a nearby rehab center.

CAUSES OF ALCOHOLISM

Different causes can cause a disorder of alcohol use (AUD). After drinking alcohol for a long time, the brain starts depending on alcohol to make those chemicals. It makes it hard for heavy drinkers to quit and can cause unpleasant symptoms of withdrawal.

Alcoholism has several common causes: biological factors, environmental factors, social factors and psychological factors. Here's a rundown of how each one plays a part in alcohol abuse growth.

Biological Factors

Research has demonstrated a close relationship between alcoholism and biological factors, in particular genetics and physiology. While some people may limit the amount of alcohol they drink, others are experiencing a strong desire to keep going. Alcohol gives off pleasure to some, encouraging the brain to repeat the behavior. Such repetitive actions will make you more vulnerable to developing alcoholism.

The brain also contains other molecules that can make you more vulnerable to drug misuse. For example, scientists have suggested that alcohol dependency in various parts of the chromosome may be correlated with up to 51 genes. When such genes are passed down across generations, members of the family are much more likely to develop alcohol disorders.

Environmental Factors

A potential link between your environment and AUD danger has been explored in recent years by studies. For instance, several studies have investigated whether the proximity of an individual to alcohol retail stores or bars influences their chances of alcoholism or not. It is said that people living near to alcohol establishments have a more optimistic view of drinking and are more likely to engage in the practice.

Also, alcohol suppliers flood the general population with commercials. Most of these commercials depict alcohol as a soothing, fun, and appropriate pastime. Alcohol ads in the United States grew by more than 400 percent in just four decades – between 1971 and 2011.

Another consideration in environmental factors is wages, which may also play a role in the amount of alcohol a person consumes. Contrary to common opinion, people who come from wealthier neighborhoods are more likely to drink than those living under the poverty line. The recent study of Gallup 's annual drinking patterns found that about 78 percent of people with an annual household income of $75,000 or more drink alcohol. It is slightly higher than the 45 percent of people who drink alcohol and have less than $30,000 in annual household income.

Social Factors

Social factors may contribute to the views of an individual on drinking. Many of your behaviors are influenced by your culture, religion, family, and work, including drinking. Family plays the greatest role in the probability of a person developing alcoholism. Children who are exposed from an early age to alcohol abuse are more at risk of falling into a dangerous drinking pattern.

Starting at college or a new job may also increase your vulnerability to alcoholism. You're trying to make new friends during these periods and to establish relationships with peers. The urge to fit in and be well-liked will cause you to take part in activities you wouldn't usually take part in. You're going to the happy hour company before you know it, drinking more often and even craving alcohol after a hard-working day, these are all warning signs of AUD.

Psychological Factors

Various psychological factors can increase the chances of drinking heavily. All approach issues in their special fashion. Whether you deal with these emotions will however influence other behavioral traits. Persons with high stress, anxiety, depression, and other mental health problems, for example, are more vulnerable to alcohol abuse. Alcohol is also used to mask emotions in these types of conditions and to ease the symptoms of psychiatric disorders.

200

Drinking can become normal over time and lead to an AUD. The more you resort to alcohol to relieve pain and suffering emotions, the more accepting the body is to the drug and depends on its effects. Concurrent misuse of alcohol and mental health disorders, such as depression, anxiety, and schizophrenia, can cause a variety of significant side effects. Each should be handled independently by a medical practitioner to resolve these problems.

Alcoholism Risk Factors

The potential for developing alcoholism includes several risk factors. Risk factors for alcoholism do not mean that you are going to develop a drinking problem, however, they should serve as a preventive measure. When you have one or more risk factors, speak to a health care provider about warning signs of alcoholism and opportunities for prevention.

Several common alcohol abuse risk factors include:

Drinking at an Early Age

Later in life, particularly in your 20s and 30s, experimenting with alcohol at a young age can lead to problems. This is particularly true when teenagers often engage in binge drinking. While drinking early can increase the risk of alcohol addiction, alcoholism at any age can affect anyone.

Family History with Alcohol Addiction

Growing up with family members and close relatives who are suffering from alcoholism raises the risk for future generations of substance abuse. You can look at alcohol use differently when you're surrounded by people who drink heavily and fall victim to bad habits.

High Levels of Stress

Drinking to reduce stress can easily turn into a problem. Doctors, nurses, emergency rescue personnel, construction workers, and the military provide job fields that are more likely to experience high-stress rates due to long hours and strenuous activities. To avoid alcohol abuse, professionals in any industry need to find other ways to de-stress.

Peer Pressure

If a partner or a good friend drinks regularly, you may be more likely to join them. Being affected by social pressure can lead to drinking issues down the road, as well as other health risks caused by excessive consumption of alcohol. Offer to be designated driver instead of having the urge to drink.

Frequent Alcohol Consumption Over a Long Period

If drinking too much is a trend, the chances of having an alcohol-related problem are greatly increased. The more you drink, the more tolerance the body has toward alcohol. Tolerance means you're going to need more alcohol to feel the same impact you've felt with less.

Why People Relapse

It requires time and effort to be safe, and to preserve your sobriety. Unfortunately, after treatment for alcohol addiction, some people relapse. Triggers, like a group of drinking buddies, any behaviors or circumstances, may cause someone to slip back into old drinking habits.

Relapsing doesn't mean you have failed and can't beat alcoholism. It will make you aware of the causes and can encourage you to seek more assistance from a counselor or support group. Participating in continuing treatment services gives you a better chance of long-term sobriety than those with rehabilitation programs don't maintain recovery.

Reasons why some people relapse are :

- Social pressure

- Stress and anxiety

- Old habits

- Mental or emotional instability

- Frustration or Anger

- The temptation to feel drunk again

Treatment constitutes the first step towards a healthier future. Professionals in drug treatment collaborate with you to build a customized, structured rehabilitation plan with measurable goals. Comprehensive treatment plans can include inpatient or outpatient therapy, drug-assisted therapy, counseling, and social support.

CHAPTER 8

EFFECTS OF ALCOHOL

What Are the Effects of Alcohol?

Each person is different, thus, alcohol effects vary from person to person. Although some individuals may be able to restrict their consumption, others are having a difficult time regulating their alcohol use.

To better understand the effects of drinking, first, you should know what constitutes an alcoholic drink. One drink is accepted as:

- 12 fluid ounces of beer-about 5% alcohol

- Seven or nine malt liquor fluid ounces – around seven percent alcohol

- Five ounces of wine– around 12 percent alcohol

- One and a half fluid ounces of 80% proof distilled spirits (vodka, rum, gin, tequila, whisky, etc.)-an estimated 40% alcohol.

Alcohol 's effects can be affected by a variety of risk factors such as the amount consumed, medical history of the patient, alcohol tolerance, as well as other substances associated with alcohol-legal or illegal.

When you, or a loved one, are suffering from drug symptoms, it is time to seek treatment. Our recovery experts will put you in touch with top-rated alcohol rehabilitation facilities which will help you get back on track with your life. Call us now to find out about rehab services and other recuperation tools.

Understanding Blood Alcohol Content (BAC)

The blood-alcohol level of an individual (BAC) determines the drug's effect on the central nervous system. Some who have built up alcohol tolerance can drink more than those who have a lower tolerance.

You can encounter an array of side effects ranging from mild complications to more serious ones, depending on your BAC. Higher BAC levels, for example, appear to come with transient side effects that will subside within a few hours. However, as the level of BAC increases, the symptoms are even more severe and can pose life threats.

Here's a breakdown of different BAC percentages along with their symptoms:

BAC: 0.033-0.12 Percent

- Less anxiety

- Higher self-confidence

- Improvement in mood

- Flushing of the face

- Impairment of judgment

- Lack of fine motor coordination

- Shorter attention span

BAC: 0.09-0.25 Percent

- Delayed motor reaction

- Loss of memory and lack of comprehension

- Sedation

- Balance problems and ataxia

- Blurred vision and sensation impairment

BAC 0.25-0.40 Percent

- In and out of consciousness or complete unconsciousness

- Slowed heart rate

- Amnesia during the events while intoxicated

- Staggering gait

- Respiratory depression

- Vomiting with aspiration

- Incontinence of urine

  BAC 0.35-0.80 Percent

- Death

- Lack of pupillary response to light

- Life-threatening respiratory depression

- Severe decrease in heart rate

- Comatose

How Alcohol Abuse Affects the Body

Abuse of alcohol can affect both inside and outside your body. Even if you cannot see the harm done to your internal organs by drinking, it is important not to ignore the warning signs of alcoholism. The adverse effects are often not detected until much later in life, making it impossible to remedy many complications in safety.

Although any organ in your body can feel the effects of alcohol, some are at greater risk of significant damage. The best approach now and in the future to avoid health complications is to stop drinking with the support of a qualified treatment program.

BRAIN

One can easily feel the effects of alcohol on the brain. Not only can alcohol cause acute problems such as memory loss and balance, but it can also lead to long-term, often permanent side-effects.

Prolonged use of alcohol can interfere with the functioning of the brain, as well as damaging it. Damage to various regions of the brain, especially the cerebellum, limbic system, and cerebral cortex, can have a major effect on communication pathways of the body. For instance, the cerebellum manages the motor skills of your body. If alcohol affects this brain region, you are more likely to experience a lack of control as well as problems of memory and emotional response.

HEART

The heart is particularly vulnerable to the adverse effects of drug use. Heavy drinking can weaken the heart over time, affecting how oxygen and nutrients are delivered to other vital organs in your body. Excessive consumption of alcohol will increase triglyceride levels-a form of fat in your blood. Large triglyceride levels lead to the risk of developing harmful health problems such as diabetes and heart disease.

Many of the early cardiovascular symptoms, such as elevated blood pressure and an irregular pulse, can lead to a variety of future problems. Long-term effects of excessive drinking could include cardiomyopathy, stroke, and sudden heart attack.

LIVER

Heavy drinkers face dangerous, potentially life-threatening liver problems. The liver breaks down alcohol when you drink, and extracts it from the blood. And in a short time, too much alcohol will overpower the mechanism of metabolism and lead to a fatty liver. Fatty liver is a chronic condition that involves the accumulation of bad liver fats. Obesity is one of the most extreme fatty liver causes. It may also cause hepatic insufficiency and type

2 diabetes.

Alcoholic hepatitis, fibrosis, and cirrhosis are other severe liver problems linked with chronic and heavy consumption of alcohol. All of these conditions are treatable, a proper medical diagnosis and comprehensive care plan will be required.

PANCREAS

The pancreas is part of the digestive process and helps to regulate blood sugar levels in your body. Drinking alcohol over many years can start to damage your pancreas and cause lasting complications to your health. The early stages of many pancreatic disorders are, unfortunately, still unfelt and often left untreated.

Long-term alcohol abuse can eventually cause swelling of the blood vessels surrounding the pancreas, leading to pancreatitis. This significantly increases the risk of developing a pancreatic cancer-a form of cancer that is rapidly spreading and very dangerous. Acute pancreatic damage signs may include abdominal pain, vomiting, nausea, rapid heart rate, and fever. Although medications and other treatment strategies may help control pancreatitis symptoms, restoring health is quite difficult.

SIDE EFFECTS OF ALCOHOL ABUSE

There are various long- and short-term side effects linked to excessive drinking. The symptoms you may experience often depend on how much alcohol you have been consuming. For example, lower to moderate levels of consumption usually entail less severe effects than drinking more.

Several side effects of substance dependence in the short term include:

- Vision impairment

- Slurred speech

- Lack of coordination

- Extreme shifts in mood

- Memory lapses

- Lack of coordination

- Slowed breathing

While some people may encounter numerous side effects, some may face fewer problems than others. The consequences of heavy drinking, however, affect more than the person dealing with alcohol addiction – it affects the people around them. It can have an immediate impact on your friends, family, and colleagues. Even the short-term effects of alcohol can cause extensive damage, from driving under the influence (DUI) to accidental self-harm.

There are also long-term effects, in addition to the short-term, noticeable side effects of alcoholism. Individuals who drink alcohol for a prolonged period are at higher risk of these conditions arising. Within months and years, signs slowly emerge.

The long-term side effects that heavy drinking entails are:

- Cardiovascular diseases

- Nerve damage

- Respiratory infections

- Ulcer

- Liver disease

- Cancer

Such long-term side effects of alcoholism may have an impact on many aspects of your life such as family or partner relationship issues, legal problems, financial problems, and bad performance at work or in school.

Choosing to overcome alcoholism is a very significant choice in the life of a person. When you quit drinking under the care of professionally trained treatment providers, it's important to do so safely. If you or a loved one are suffering the short-term or long-term consequences of substance addiction, they will help you explore the various treatment options. Give us a call today to get your recovery journey underway.

ALCOHOL ABUSE TREATMENT

Alcohol addiction can easily ruin somebody's potential aspirations and dreams. There are specialized alcohol treatment programs across the country that help millions of people surmount alcoholism every year. Treatment centers with personalized rehabilitation plans in place provide exclusive services, therapies, and activities to match your needs. You can learn how to manage triggers, avoid the temptation to drink, and other strategies to help you maintain sobriety during your recovery program.

STOP ALCOHOLISM NOW

It's time to end the misuse of alcohol and lead a safe and happy life. A rehab service will help you identify treatment options for drug addiction, tailored to your unique needs.

CHAPTER 9

HOW TO BREAK A BAD HABIT (AND REPLACE IT WITH A GOOD ONE)

Poor habits are interrupting your life and preventing you from reaching your goals. They put your safety at risk-both psychologically and physically. And they are wasting your time and your energy. Why are we even doing them, then? And most importantly, will you do something about it?

I've written before about the science of how behaviors develop, so let's now concentrate on the practice of making real-world changes. How do you eradicate your negative habits, and then stick to healthy ones? I still don't have all the answers but keep reading, and I'm going to share what I've heard about breaking a bad habit.

What causes bad habits?

Two things trigger most of your bad habits ... Stress and boredom. Bad habits are, most of the time, simply a way to cope with tension and boredom. It can be an easy answer to stress and boredom, from chewing your nails to overspending on a shopping spree to drinking every weekend to wasting time on the internet.

Yet that shouldn't be the way it is. You should teach yourself new and healthier ways to cope with stress and depression, which you can use to replace those bad habits. Of course, frequently the underlying problems trigger the tension or frustration that is on the surface. These issues can be hard to think about, but if you are serious about making changes, then you must be honest with yourself.

Are there any convictions or explanations behind the poor habit? Is there anything more profound — a fear, an occurrence, or a limiting belief— that causes you to hang on to something bad for you? To conquer this, it is important to consider the causes of bad habits.

You're not eliminating a bad habit; you are replacing it.

All the habits you have right now — whether good or bad — are for a reason in your life. These behaviors provide you with a benefit in some way, even if they are otherwise bad for you.

The gain is often psychological, as it is with smoking or drugs. Even when you live in a relationship that's terrible for you, it's miserable. And your bad behavior is in many situations an easy way to cope with stress. For example, you can bite your nails, pull your hair, tap your foot or clench your jaw.

These "benefits" or explanations often refer to minor bad habits.

Opening your email inbox, for example, as soon as you turn on your computer might make you feel linked. Looking at all those emails at the same time kills your efficiency, splits your focus, and overwhelms you with tension. No, it doesn't make you feel like you're "missing out" ... and so you do it again. Since bad habits have some form of benefit in your life, it's really hard to just remove them. (This is why simple advice such as ', please stop doing it' never works.)

You will then substitute a bad habit with a new habit that offers similar value. For example, if you smoke when you get stressed, then when that happens, it's a bad plan to "just stop smoking" Instead of smoking a cigarette, you should come up with a better way to cope with stress and introduce the new behavior.

In other words, bad habits answer some of your life 's needs. So, it's easier for that reason to replace your bad habits with a healthy activity that serves the same need. If you just plan to cut bad habits without replacing them, you will have some unmet needs, and it will be hard to adhere to a "just don't do it" routine for a long time.

HOW TO BREAK A BAD HABIT

Below are some helpful suggestions to break your bad habits and focus on the process in your own way.

1. Choose a substitute for your bad habit. You need to have a plan in advance as to how you'll respond when facing the stress or boredom that prompts your bad habits. What will you do when you are getting the urge to smoke? (Example: use breathing exercises.) What do you do when Facebook is making you dawdle? (Example: write a paragraph for work.) Whatever it is and whatever you're struggling with, you need to have a plan for what

215

you're going to do, rather than your bad habit.

2. Cut the maximum number of stimuli available. If you smoke when you're drinking, do not go to the lounge. If you are in the house eating cookies, then throw them all away. If the first thing you do is pick up the TV remote when you sit on the sofa, then hide the remote in a separate space in the wardrobe. Make it easier to break bad habits in yourself by avoiding the things that cause them.

3. Join hands with someone else. So how much do you want to take a private diet? And maybe you're "quitting smoking" ... but you've kept it to yourself? (No one will see you fail that way, right?) Instead, pair up with somebody and quit. The two of you should keep each other accountable and celebrate with your victories. Knowing others expect you to be better is a powerful motivator.

4. Surround yourself with people living the way you want to be living. You don't have to cut off your old friends but don't underestimate the ability to discover new ones.

5. Visualize yourself effectively. Watch yourself throw away the cigarettes or buy healthy food or wake up early. Whatever the bad habit is that you're trying to smash, kill it, smile and enjoy your success. See how you develop a new identity.

6. You don't have to be someone; you just have to go back to the old you. So often we assume that we have to become an entirely new person to break our bad habits. The reality is you have

216

it in yourself to be someone without your bad habits. It's just doubtful that you've had these bad habits all of your life. You don't have to quit smoking; you just have to go back to being a non-smoker. You don't have to turn yourself into a good person; you just need to get back to being a good person. Even if it was years ago, you've lived without this bad habit, which means you can do it again most certainly.

7. Using the term "but" to practice negative self-talk. One thing about fighting bad habits is punishing yourself for not behaving better. It's easy to tell yourself how bad you feel each time you mess up or make a mistake. Whenever this occurs, put "but" in the sentence.

- "I'm overweight and out of shape, but a few months from now, I will be in shape."

- "I'm dumb, and no one respects me, so I'm learning to improve user skills."

- "I'm a failure, but sometimes everyone fails."

8. Plan for failure. Now and then we mess everyone up. And prepare for it rather than beating yourself up over a mistake. We all get off course, what distinguishes top performers from everyone else is that they very easily get back on track. Read this article for a variety of tactics that will help you come back when you make a mistake.

Where to go from here

If you are looking for the first step to break your bad habits, then I would suggest that you start with knowledge. The way you feel about your bad habits is easy to get caught up in. You may feel guilty or waste your time thinking of how you want things to be ... but these feelings take you away from what is going on.

It's understanding that will show you how progress can be made.

- Really, when does your bad habit happen?

- How often do you do it every day?

- Where are you from?

- What are you?

- What triggers and causes the behavior to take off?

Only monitoring these issues will increase your knowledge of the conduct and give you thousands of ideas to stop it.

It takes time and energy to break bad habits, but also it takes perseverance. Most people who end up breaking their bad habits try and struggle repeatedly before they get it to work. You may not have instant success, but that doesn't mean you can't have it at all.

CHAPTER 10

I STOPPED DRINKING FOR 30 DAYS— HERE IS WHAT IT DID TO MY MIND, BODY, AND SKIN

I t was Memorial Day weekend. A close mate, Victoria, and I had jetted up to Santa Barbara to celebrate the start of summer for a day of wine tasting. We had spent the day strolling from winery to winery, tasting a variety of pinots, both red and white, and both of us were sporting a festive buzz on our last day of tasting. It was more of a goodbye party because I'd embark on a sober 30 days starting June 1.

I almost couldn't believe it, **but I didn't give myself so much as a sip of a friend's rosé for the entire month of June.** I know it doesn't sound like a big deal for some people to go 30 days without alcohol, but I'd never done it before. I hadn't gone more than a dry week since high school when I thought about it. Alcohol was already playing a relatively present part of my life at 24. I wasn't drunk as I was in college (my gut-wrenching hangovers wouldn't encourage that).

Yet alcohol was always closely tied up with my life. As an experiment, I wanted to see just how, without it, I could work.

Victoria and I were going out to the outdoor patio of the winery to finish our final glass when we stumbled (quite literally) across a chalkboard sign that read, "No wine past this point." I stood at the front steps and drank my last drink, and we took a ride from Lyft. The next day I will wake up a sober woman.

Why I Quit Drinking?

I want to dig a little further into why I wanted to go booze-free before getting into my 30-day experiment. First of all, I was willing to ease some of alcohol's harmful effects that I still bear.

For starters, I would have started eating a plant-based diet about six months before, and a lot of the vegan community is sober as well. It goes hand in hand with a mentality that is clean-eating. The vegans I know who don't drink seem to be extraordinarily vibrant and healthy, and I was curious to see if alcohol giving up would do the same for me.

I was also inspired by tales from friends who had gone without drinking long stretches before. My boyfriend has spent 30 days refusing alcohol, and the results have been nothing short of spectacular. He lost weight, his eczema and rosacea subsided, and in the end, he appeared a happier, more successful individual overall. He told me the first week was tough, but you don't even miss the alcohol anymore after that. You don't even know why you liked this.

And because it all appealed to me, eating less, feeling brighter, and having healthy skin, I knew I was all-in to give this a shot.

Benefits of Quitting Alcohol

- Higher energy levels

- Better quality of sleep

- Improved skin health and hydration

According to registered dietitian Jenny Champion, sugar cravings, excess calorie consumption, dehydrated skin, fuzzy concentration, and bad moods can be caused by just casual drinking. Not only does alcohol produce almost twice as many calories as vegetables, but blended drinks are also full of sugar fruit juice — so you're missing something if you watch your diet but don't work out at nights. But alcohol doesn't only trigger sugar cravings, it flat out makes you crave food. Cravings plus the lowered inhibitions that come with alcohol are a perfect recipe for drinks loaded with carb and sugar but not a perfect recipe to feel better.

Not only does alcohol contain twice as many calories as carbohydrates, but mixed drinks are often full of sugary fruit juice.

Thinking of the next morning, who among us got drunk and forgot to take off our makeup or forget our skincare routine in favor of a makeup wipe? Just being unwavering with skincare benefits the skin. It's well known, however, that alcohol itself has adverse effects on your skin. A by-product of alcohol metabolization is acetaldehyde, which not only dehydrates your body but also your skin. Unfortunately, no amount of water you drink can do away with this particular negative effect; the best you can expect to do is to dilute it. Booze also dilates your pores and acts as an inflammatory, releasing histamine, which is why your skin gets so red and blotchy and stays so bad a few days later.

Finally, when I thought deeply about it, it just seemed odd to me that something as easy as a drink could have such life-changing and mind-altering effects on people. It seems that alcohol has set this spell upon us. For so many reasons, we empty our glasses: as payment, as a medicine, as social lubrication, as an escape. When there's something positive going on, we drink. When we drink something bad happens. Sometimes we drink for no reason at all. I've decided that I no longer wanted to be under that influence.

What to Expect

It has to be stated: My sober month has been tough. I was most excited at the beginning to see the positive effects it would have on my skin. That might be irrational, but I wanted major improvements to be observed immediately: a brightened skin, a dewier finish, fewer blemishes. When nothing, a week into the challenge seemed different, I started questioning why I did it in the first place.

Going an alcohol-free month also teaches you about the drinking habit. This is important information if you want to try to cut back on alcohol in the future again. I find that I do often drink three to four nights a week, but when I do, I prefer only to have one or two glasses. When I go past two glasses on those occasions, that is when alcohol starts to be a problem for me.

To be honest, it's hard to tell whether or not the huge blemish on my cheek before I started drinking was linked to alcohol. I've recently had a skin problem that rivaled the one at the end of my sober month. A beautician later told me my imperfections probably had more to do with hormones and stress than anything else. I know, a little bit anti-climactic. But that rough, pinkish patch of skin right next to my eye was certainly alcohol-related. It was a nasty spot of eczema which I had been fighting for nearly a year. My eczema is not painful or itching; it's just unsightly. The scaly texture is such that I can't hide it with makeup, and even prescription steroid creams couldn't make it go away. To date, the only treatment that has worked to clear my eczema is giving up alcohol. About two weeks in, for the first time in months, the inflamed, crinkled skin softens. Certified nutritionist Dana James suggests that a reaction to yeast may be causing my eczema. "You've lowered your contact with it by taking the alcohol out and reducing the symptoms," she told me.

A by-product of alcohol metabolization is acetaldehyde, which not only dehydrates your body but your skin too.

Although at the end of the month my eczema re-emerged slightly, that initial disappearing act was substantial. I also found that the parts of my face, which tended to get flaky looked a little more hydrated by week two of my experiment.

Actually, for the last two weeks of my sober month, my skin quality appeared to remain relatively constant. Yet after the 30 days had finished and I started to drink again, it quickly returned to its unhealthy state. To put it plainly, **there is no questioning the influence of alcohol on our skin—you just have to be aware to see that.**

Side Effects

I'm going to say something that could upset you but not even as much as it disappointed me: I gained weight during my month without alcohol —around 3 pounds, to be exact. I think the main reason is that during those 30 days I found myself eating out in restaurants a lot — three or four nights a week, indulging in rich Thai curries and oily plates of pasta. I convinced myself that by not drinking, I was saving so many calories that I could eat pretty much anything I wanted. The reasoning hasn't served me well. Of course, the meals were plant-based and followed by sparkling water instead of wine, but it was enough to tip the scale to eat those large portions of restaurant food. (As a reminder, I don't personally own a scale and rarely weigh myself; I did so purely for this experiment's sake.) Speaking of dining out, it did not seem like my social life was suffering from my sobriety, as I was concerned. We simply decided to grab a bite to eat instead of a drink at a bar when making plans with friends. (This also led to my heightened consumption of restaurant calories.)

Each time I got home at a respectable hour, never woke up hungover, and everybody was always having fun. Waking up every day feeling healthy and well-rested has been one of my favorite aspects of not drinking for a month. As I have said, these days, I seldom get drunk enough to cause crippling hangovers. Yet at times, two drinks are all that's needed to make me feel foggy and bloated the next day. I didn't get up earlier than usual, but every night I certainly squeezed in an extra half hour. Winding down with a drink after work always inspired me to go to bed before. This had to do more with the boredom—10 p.m. Will roll around and joyful buzz without any kind of light

The Final Takeaway

I'd be lying if I said I wasn't disappointed that after 30 days without drinking, there were no more drastic changes to my body. All the experiences of friends of mine seemed so much more worthwhile. I believe the reason for this has to do with another unexpected but important lesson that I learned from this experiment.

A fading eczema patch and an additional 30 minutes of sleep are no doubt useful rewards. But the most remarkable thing I've learned from my alcohol-free 30 days — the thing that made it all worth doing — is that it taught me exactly what function alcohol serves in my life.

During the month, there were two occasions when I missed the most alcohol. The first came at the end of a hard workday after coming in the door when all I wanted was to put my feet up and have a glass of wine. The other one was when I was in a big group during social outings, and everyone else was drinking but me. For different purposes, everybody uses alcohol, and obviously, these are mine: I use alcohol as a small, private reward for myself and as a way of bonding in large social settings. When something frustrating or bad happened, I didn't crave a cocktail. When I felt anxious and wanted to relax, I didn't miss it on a date night with my boyfriend or during awkward social circumstances. These are not the roles played by alcohol in my life. So, I'm really curious to know that.

So, I've put myself on a strict two-drink maximum since my 30-day experiment. This has become a much better way for me to make sure I'm drinking in moderation, given my drinking habits.

After all, it's possible to lead a healthy lifestyle as a moderate drinker, according to experts (as long as you don't struggle with an addiction or drinking problem, that is). "If you're living an active and balanced lifestyle that involves a diet rich in nutrients, the occasional drink shouldn't be a concern," promises John Ford, a Find Your Trainer personal trainer. The trick is to determine what function alcohol is serving in your life and fix any harmful behaviors. That's just what helped me for a month, going sober.

In the end, I didn't lose ten years off my face or 10 pounds off my body through my 30 days without alcohol. But it enabled me to learn more about my personality, my conduct, and my health. For me, that's something worth clinking a glass to.

CHAPTER 11

ALCOHOL WITHDRAWAL SYMPTOMS

What Is Alcohol Withdrawal?

When you drink alcohol regularly for weeks, months, or years when you quit or severely cut down on how much you drink, you might have both mental and physical issues. This is termed withdrawal from alcohol. Symptoms may be mild to severe.

When you drink just once in a while then you stop, it is unlikely you will have signs of withdrawal. However, if you have been through alcohol withdrawal once, the next time you call it quits, you are more likely to go through it again.

What Causes It?

Alcohol has what physicians call a depressive effect on the system. It slows the functioning of the brain and changes the way your nerves send out messages.

Over time, the central nervous system adjusts to still having alcohol around every time. The body is working hard to keep the brain alert and keep the nerves communicating with each other.

When the level of alcohol abruptly decreases, the brain stays in that keyed-up state. That is what triggers withdrawal.

227

What Are the Symptoms?

They can vary from mild to serious. What happens depends on how much and how long you've been drinking alcohol.

Generally, the mild signs start as early as 6 hours after you put down your bottle. Can include:

- Headache

- Shaky hands

- Anxiety

- Nausea

- Insomnia

- Vomiting

- Sweating

More serious problems range from 12 to 24-hour hallucinations after the last drink to seizures within the first two days after you stop. You can see, feel or hear stuff that doesn't exist.

That's not the same as delirium tremens or DTs. DTs typically start 48 to 72 hours after you put the glass down. Such symptoms include intense visions and delusions. Only about 5 percent of people with withdrawal from alcohol have them. Those that do may also have:

- Racing heart

- Confusion

- High blood pressure

- Heavy sweating

- Fever

How Is Withdrawal Diagnosed?

When the doctor suspects you might have withdrawal, he'll ask you questions about your history of drinking, and whether you've stopped recently. He will want to know if you have ever experienced withdrawal before.

He'll talk about your symptoms too. He'll be checking for any medical problems during an assessment to see whether they may be to blame.

Treatment

Your doctor will direct you about the type of care you need. If you have a serious health problem or have had extreme withdrawals in the past, you would generally need little more than a supportive atmosphere to get you through it this includes:

- Soft lighting

- A quiet place

- Healthy food and lots of fluids

- A positive, supportive atmosphere

- Limited contact with people

When your blood pressure, pulse, or body temperature increases, or if you have more serious symptoms such as seizures and hallucinations, seek urgent medical attention (dial 911). Your doctor may prescribe medication for the inpatient and medications.

Popular medications include benzodiazepines that help relieve symptoms such as anxiety, insomnia, and seizures. Along with other medications, you can even take anti-seizure medicines and antipsychotics.

Can You Prevent It?

Treating withdrawal of alcohol is a short-term remedy that does not solve the core problem. When discussing pain relief with your doctor, seeking treatment for substance abuse or dependency is a smart idea. You can get advice from the doctor to help you avoid drinking.

CHAPTER 12
ALCOHOL WITHDRAWAL SYNDROME

The scope of symptoms of alcohol withdrawal varies from mild symptoms such as fatigue and tremulousness to serious problems such as hallucinations during withdrawal and delirium tremens. While the history and physical examination are typically adequate to diagnose alcohol withdrawal syndrome, there may be similar signs in other circumstances. Most patients with withdrawal from alcohol can be treated as outpatients safely and effectively. Pharmacological interventions include the use of alcohol responsive drugs. Benzodiazepines, the agents of choice, can be administered on a schedule that is set or caused by symptoms. Carbamazepine is a safe alternative to a benzodiazepine in ambulatory care of patients with mild to moderate symptoms of withdrawal from alcohol. Drugs such as haloperidol, beta-blockers, clonidine, and phenytoin can be used in the treatment of withdrawal symptoms as adjuncts to benzodiazepine. Alcohol detox therapy should be followed by alcohol dependency therapy.

In 1992, approximately 13.8 million Americans (7.4 percent of the U.S. adult population) met the alcohol abuse or dependence criteria as specified in the Mental Disorders Diagnostic and Statistical Manual, Fourth Edition, Text Review (DSM-IV-TR). In 2000, 226,000 patients were discharged from short-stay hospitals (excluding Veteran Affairs and other federal hospitals) . So, up to 2 million Americans may experience symptoms of alcohol withdrawal every year.

Pathophysiology

Several mechanisms mediate drug withdrawal syndrome. The brain maintains neurochemical equilibrium by neurotransmitters which are inhibitory and excitatory. The major neurotransmitter inhibitory is π-aminobutyric acid (GABA), works with GABA-alpha (GABA-A)

One of the biggest exciting neurotransmitters is glutamate which acts through the neuroreceptor of N-methyl-D-aspartate (NMDA).

Alcohol increases GABA's effect on GABA-A neuroreceptors, resulting in reduced overall excitability throughout the brain. Chronic alcohol consumption results in a compensatory reduction in GABA-A neuroreceptor response to GABA, as shown by the increasing tolerance of alcohol impact.

Alcohol activates the neuroreceptors of NMDA, and prolonged exposure to alcohol results in these receptors being regulated upwards. Abrupt cessation of exposure to alcohol results in brain hyperexcitability, as alcohol-inhibited receptors are no longer inhibited. Hyperexcitability of the brain clinically expresses itself

232

as fear, irritability, agitation, and tremors. Extreme symptoms include hallucinations with alcohol withdrawal and tremors with delirium.

The "kindling" effect is an important concept in both alcohol dependence and alcohol withdrawal; the term refers to the long-lasting changes that occur in neurons following repeated detoxification. Recurrent detoxification is postulated to increase addictive thoughts or the craving for alcohol. Kindling describes the finding that subsequent periods of alcohol withdrawal appear to intensify slowly.

While the importance of kindling in the withdrawal of alcohol is being debated, this phenomenon may be significant in the selection of drugs for withdrawal care. When certain medicines decrease the enhanced effect, they may become favored agents.

Withdrawal Symptoms

Table 2 lists the continuum of withdrawal symptoms and the period for these symptoms to occur following cessation of alcohol use. Alcohol withdrawal symptoms typically apply proportionately to the amount of drug intake and the duration of a patient's recent pattern of drinking. Most patients in any episode of alcohol withdrawal have a broad set of symptoms.

There can be mild withdrawal effects when the patient still has a detectable amount of alcohol in the blood. These symptoms may include sleeplessness, mild anxiety, and tremor. Alcoholic hallucinosis patients experience visual, auditory, or tactile hallucinations but otherwise have strong sensory faculties.

Withdrawal seizures are more common in patients with a history of repeated detoxifying episodes. Whether seizures are focal, if there is no clear history of recent abstinence from drinking, if seizures occur more than 48 hours after the patient's last drink, or whether the patient has a history of fever or injuries, factors other than alcohol withdrawal should be considered.

The delirium of alcohol withdrawal, or delirium tremens, is characterized by the clouding of consciousness and hallucinations. Delirium tremor episodes have a mortality rate of 1 to 5 percent. Risk factors for the development of alcohol withdrawal include concurrent acute medical illness, daily heavy alcohol consumption, history of delirium tremens or older age, withdrawal seizures, abnormal liver function, and more severe withdrawal symptoms on presentation.

Evaluation of the Patient in Alcohol Withdrawal

History and physical exam determine the diagnosis and extent of withdrawal from alcohol. Important historical details include the quantity of alcoholic intake, length of consumption of alcohol, the period since last drink, past withdrawals of alcohol, the existence of related medical or psychiatric problems, and abuse of other agents. The physical examination will determine, in addition to detecting withdrawal symptoms, potential complicating medical problems, including arrhythmias, congestive heart failure, coronary artery disease, gastrointestinal bleeding, allergies, liver

234

disease, weakness of the nervous system, and pancreatitis. Basic lab examinations include a full blood count, liver function checks, urine drug examination, and blood alcohol and electrolyte level determination.

The revised scale of the Clinical Institute Withdrawal Assessment for Alcohol (CIWA-Ar) is a validated 10-point evaluation tool that can be used to measure the severity of alcohol withdrawal syndrome and to track and treat patient's withdrawal (Figure 1). CIWA-Ar scores of 8 points or less correspond to mild withdrawal, scores of 9 to 15 points correspond to severe withdrawal. The clinical image should be considered when using the CIWA-Ar since medical and psychological problems can resemble symptoms of alcohol withdrawal. Additionally, certain medicines (e.g., beta-blockers) may moderate these symptoms.

Differential Diagnosis

Alcohol withdrawal syndrome and other conditions may be confused. Thyrotoxicosis, anticholinergic drug overdose, and the use of amphetamine or cocaine may lead to symptoms of increased sympathetic activity and mental changes. Infection or illness of the central nervous system may cause hallucinations and changes in mental status. Removal from other sedative-hypnotic agents induces symptoms similar to those that occur in the condition of withdrawal from alcohol.

Goals of Treatment

The American Society of Addiction Medicine specifies three

specific aims for the detoxification of alcohol and other substances: (1) "providing a healthy removal from the drug(s) of dependency and enabling the patient to become drug-free;" (2) "providing a compassionate removal and thereby maintaining the integrity of the patient;" and (3) "preparing the patient for the continued treatment of his or her dependency on the medication."

General Care

Any blood gas, electrolytes, or nutritional irregularities should be corrected. In patients with extreme, withdrawal may require intravenous fluids due to excessive loss of fluid through hyperthermia, sweating, and vomiting. Intravenous fluids in patients with less serious withdrawal should not be regularly administered, as these patients may become overhydrated.

It has not been shown to improve withdrawal symptoms through regular administration of magnesium sulfate, but supplementation is necessary if a patient is in hypomagnesemia. During alcohol detox therapy multivitamins and thiamine (100 mg per day) should be given. If intravenous fluids are administered, thiamine (100 mg intravenously) should be given before glucose is released, to prevent Wernicke's encephalopathy from developing.

Medication Regimens

Drugs can be administered using fixed-schedule or symptom-triggered regimens (Table 3). Benzodiazepine doses are administered at regular intervals with a fixed-schedule regimen, and additional doses of the drug are administered as required depending on the severity of the withdrawal symptoms. Medication is offered in a symptom-triggered regime only if the CIWA-Ar score is greater than 8 points.

Symptom-triggered regimes have been shown to result in the administration of less overall medication and to provide a shorter period of treatment. In one randomized, double-blind clinical trial,11 patients in the symptom-triggered group received an average of 100 mg of chlordiazepoxide. In contrast, patients in the fixed-schedule group received an average of 425 mg. The mean period of treatment in the symptom-triggered group was nine hours, compared with 68 hours in the fixed-schedule group. Patients were removed from the study if they had underlying medical or mental disorders from any cause that involved hospitalization or seizure

Another trial yielded similar findings, with patients receiving an average of 231.4 mg of oxazepam in the fixed-schedule group and those receiving an average of 37.5 mg in the symptom-triggered group. For the patients in the group affected by the symptoms, 61 percent got no oxazepam. The study excluded people with severe psychological, emotional, or medical comorbidities.

The use of symptom-triggered therapy will require clinical staff training. If this instruction has not been provided, pharmacotherapy should be used on a set schedule.

Choice of Treatment Setting

Outpatient detoxification is safe and successful in most patients with mild to moderate withdrawal symptoms and costs less than inpatient care. However, certain patients should be considered for inpatient treatment irrespective of the severity of their symptoms. Indicative signs for inpatient alcohol detoxification are as follows: the history of serious withdrawal symptoms, history of withdrawal seizures or delirium tremors, numerous prior detoxifications, concomitant mental or medical disorder, recent high alcohol intake rates, pregnancy and lack of a stable support network.

When ambulatory treatment is preferred, the patient should be reviewed regularly. The patient and support person(s) should be advised on how to administer the withdrawal drug, the side effects of the drug, the possible symptoms of withdrawal, and what to do if symptoms worsen. Small amounts of withdrawal medication should be administered during each visit; thiamine and multivitamins should also be administered. Due to the lack of close supervision in outpatient care, a set schedule regime should be used.

PHARMACOLOGICAL TREATMENT OF WITHDRAWAL

Benzodiazepines

Pharmacological diagnosis of alcohol withdrawal syndrome includes the use of drugs that do not interact. Benzodiazepines are safe and effective, particularly in the prevention or treatment of seizures and delirium, and are the preferred agents for treating

238

alcohol withdrawal syndrome symptoms.

The physician's choice is dependent on the pharmacokinetics. Diazepam (Valium) and chlordiazepoxide (Librium) are long-acting drugs that have proven to be effective in treating symptoms of alcohol withdrawal. Withdrawal is quicker because of the long half-life of these drugs, and signs of rebound withdrawal are less likely to occur. Lorazepam (Ativan) and oxazepam (Serax) are drugs that function intermediately and have outstanding efficacy records. Treatment with these agents, particularly the elderly and those with liver failure, may be preferable in patients who metabolize medications less effectively. Lorazepam is the only benzodiazepine whose intramuscular absorption is predictable (if intramuscular administration is necessary).

Rarely, extremely high dosages of benzodiazepines are needed to control the symptoms of withdrawal from alcohol. Dosages of diazepam as high as 2,000 mg a day were administered. Since physicians are often hesitant to prescribe extremely high dosages, undertreatment of withdrawal of alcohol is a common issue.

One randomized controlled trial (RCT)19 confirmed previous findings that carbamazepine in patients with mild to moderate symptoms is an important alternative to benzodiazepines in the treatment of alcohol withdrawal syndrome. Patients in the study received 800 mg of carbamazepine on day one, with the dosage tapered to 200 mg by day five. Carbamazepine (Tegretol) also tends to relieve drug cravings following withdrawal. It is not sedating and has little abuse potential. While carbamazepine is commonly used in Europe, its use in the United States has been restricted by a lack of adequate evidence that it prevents seizures and delirium.

ADJUNCTIVE AGENTS

In the diagnosis of alcohol withdrawal syndrome, some drugs can be effective adjuncts to benzodiazepines. These drugs should not, however, be used as monotherapy.

Haloperidol (Haldol) can be used to treat anxiety and hallucinations, and it can decrease the risk of seizures. The use of atenolol (Tenormin) in combination with oxazepam has been shown to improve symptoms faster, and more effectively alleviate drug cravings than the use of oxazepam alone.

Adjunctive treatment with a beta-blocker should be considered in patients with coronary artery disease who may not tolerate the strain on the cardiovascular system that alcohol withdrawal can impose. Clonidine (Catapres) has also been shown to enhance autonomic withdrawal symptoms. While phenytoin (Dilantin) does not treat withdrawal seizures, it is an appropriate alternative in patients with an underlying seizure disorder.

Patient Follow-Up

Alcohol withdrawal syndrome therapy should be accompanied by alcohol dependency therapy. Withdrawal therapy alone does not resolve the underlying addiction disorder, and therefore

240

provides no hope for long-term abstinence.

Brief interventions in patients with alcohol dependency are helpful in the outpatient setting but more intensive treatments can be needed in patients with alcohol dependence. It has been shown that anticonvulsant topiramate (Topamax) is an important adjunctive drug for reducing alcohol intake and abstinence in alcohol-dependent patients

After attending 12-step programs like Alcoholics Anonymous and Narcotics Anonymous, some patients produce positive results. Many patients benefit from stays in comprehensive treatment facilities which include a 12-step model, cognitive-behavioral therapy, and family therapy. Alcohol withdrawal syndrome therapy should be complemented by an individualized, intensive treatment plan, or at least as many components of a plan as the patient can handle and afford.

Future Directions

Some drugs showed early promise in treating withdrawal from alcohol. A single 10-mg dose of baclofen in one case report involving five patients resulted in relief of severe withdrawal symptoms. In a preliminary RCT, baclofen also minimized cravings in patients addicted to alcohol.

In small trials, gabapentin, which is structurally similar to GABA, was successful in treating alcohol withdrawal. The low toxicity of gabapentin makes it a promising agent. In another study, the vigabatrin anticonvulsant agent, which blocks GABA

241

transaminase irreversibly, has diminished withdrawal symptoms after just three days of treatment.

Prevention

Early identification of problem drinking allows complications to be prevented or treated, including severe withdrawal. The U.S. Preventive Services Task Force recommends screening patients through a careful history or standardized screening questionnaire for problematic drinking. Patients undergoing preoperative assessment should also be screened because the cessation of alcohol will hinder recovery from surgery. Elective surgery should be delayed until the addicted patient has had no alcohol for 7 to 10 days.

CHAPTER 13

PLANNING FOR ALCOHOL OR DRUG

RELAPSE

When you want to avoid using alcohol or narcotics, there are steps you should take to stay drug-free or sober. It's very hard to stop using substances, whether it's alcohol or drugs you're using. The first time they try very few people succeed. There is likely to be a break or a relapse.

- A drop is the first time you use the substance or drink again after you have stopped or small periods of later use.

- A relapse can't stay drug-free or drug-sober over time. It can occur if you have a series of near lapses or a lapse over a longer period leading to the heavier use of drugs or alcohol. It most often occurs a couple of months after you stop using drugs or alcohol.

If there's a slipup or relapse, that may mean you've just messed up. If that's valid for you, then accept the error and move on. Start finding out why you've relapsed and make changes in your life so it won't happen again. For support programs like Narcotics Anonymous, LifeRing, or Alcoholics Anonymous, you may even need additional medical treatment or more time.

You may have many relapses, whether you have managed to avoid using the drug on your own or sought support. Relapses typically occur less often as time goes by, and are shorter.

Have a relapse plan

Consider you may be getting a relapse. This might be easier to deal with if you think about what to do with a relapse before it happens.

Speak to support experts on what to do if you have a relapse. Such individuals can include your sponsor or your doctor, psychologist, family, colleagues, and community support. Decide who to call, where to go and what to do if a question occurs. There are people you should turn to, including your sponsor, your psychiatrist, your psychologist, or a hotline for the crisis.

Think about your triggers

Triggers are things that might cause you to have a relapse. They may include:

- **Certain people**. Running into people with whom you drank or used drugs can cause memories and a desire to use drugs or alcohol again. They might encourage you to use drugs or alcohol if you meet these people.

- **Certain places**. Walking into a bar, a friend's home or a park where you have been drinking or using drugs can cause a craving. Even being in the same area may cause some cravings.

- **Certain things**. You can connect objects to alcohol or drug use. Finding a syringe or crack pipe, for example, might cause memories.

- **Certain times**. A craving may happen on certain days or times of the day, holidays, or weather. That depends on the drug or alcohol experiences.

- **Certain smells, sounds, and sensations**. A cause may be the scent of the drug, a cigarette, or a meal. It may also trigger a longing for a rainy day, an album, or a TV program.

- **Stress.** Stress is a definite catalyst. Any situation in which you feel stress increases your chance of a relapse.

- **Certain situations**. Social events, parties, or being alone may make you think about taking a drink or trying drugs.

Writing down the causes and learning about them will help. Are any more likely than others to cause a relapse? Rank the causes most likely to cause a relapse to the least likely to cause a relapse.

Decide on how to handle your triggers. You need to avoid certain circumstances or individuals or stay away from a favorite activity or location. When you know that you can't stop a cause, bring in a friend to help you.

If you lapse or relapse

- Avoid drinking alcohol at once or taking the drug. Get rid of this thing. Leave where you are in the situation.

- Rest assured. Remember, you have a strategy, and remember how hard you've worked to stay drug-free or sober.

- Get help immediately. Call the people listed in your plan, or go to the locations specified in your plan.

- Focus on what happened after you started drinking alcohol or taking drugs. Find out what caused you to relapse and how to stop it happening again. Place that in your strategy.

CHAPTER 14

THE POWER OF POSITIVE AFFIRMATIONS

Positive affirmations are a straightforward strategy – you can use these useful phrases anywhere and everywhere (you don't have to use them loudly to make them work). Some of the main benefits of this approach are that it will improve your self-esteem. It's the same as getting a motivational coach in your head, inspiring you to put extra effort into ensuring your success.

People with low self-esteem appear to have an internal voice that is often hostile and threatening.

This negativity can be so bad that self-hatred develops in the individual. This toxic internal dialogue will drastically reduce motivation, which means that the person starts feeling powerless and hopeless. Positive words shift this inner voice's essence, so it becomes more motivating and compassionate, which can have an amazing effect.

The other great affirmations thing is they will give you the confidence to come out of your comfort zone. When you want to fulfil your full potential, you will have to force yourself beyond what you think you can achieve. Instead of positive affirmations, this desire to go the extra mile will come about.

Daily affirmations can be one of your recovery devices. These affirmations will make you feel better and more balanced when you're having a rough day or are planning for a busy week. Affirmations are a way to consciously and deliberately live your life, which many of us know nothing about. Affirmations will help you find your way back to where you want to go. They are the building blocks to help ensure a long, stable, drug and alcohol free life. Affirmations are just one of the many pieces of the puzzle that will help you get your new life together.

USING AFFIRMATIONS – POWER OF POSITIVE THINKING

You should get what's known as a toolbox in rehab. Which means you're going to have a list of strategies, coping mechanisms, action plans and skills to help you heal from daily life. While drugs and alcohol may have been your go-to method of dealing with all that life throws at you, trying to survive without such substances allows you to find new ways to get through good and bad days. Affirmations are one of the methods that many people use in recuperation.

Affirmations are a simple, regular rehabilitation resource that can be a great complement to your Alcoholics Anonymous recovery program, SMART recovery, drug treatment, or any other form of recovery pathway. Let's take a look at when and how to use them.

When we believe something for long enough, and frequently

enough, then our conscious, unconscious and subconscious minds start feeling it. As I said, "I am an alcoholic," at the outset of my sobriety, a part of my brain just didn't believe it. I repeated it before it was a part of me. So, I started to think, "I'm an alcoholic recoverer." Once again, my brain had a lot of things to think about, but finally, I started to realize that I was healing by following the steps and only doing what people said.

I would say to myself "I am a recovering addict," I wanted to change the mantra again.

I started telling the world, and mainly my head that I was a "thankful recovering addict." I wasn't thankful much of the time, but I said it enough that it is my reality now. I'm grateful, and I'm healing.

It seems to me that the self-talk is mostly negative as strangers reach AA's quarters. I think we should be asking everyone in the curriculum to start making affirmations. "I count, I am a beautiful, affectionate and loving person."

I am a much more than just an addict and accepting that is part of healing.

And I'm trying to say in a meeting, "My name is Martha, and I'm a colleague of Bill's." That's a good affirmation because it marks me as participating in the program.

There are all kinds of calming talks and motivation videos that can be found on the internet and in your local library. Wherever you are in your treatment plan, focus on calming and meditating or using creative imagination to retrain your mind and start transforming the negative self-talk into something constructive.

You're drunk and sober. Celebrate that and be thankful for being one of those still on the program.

Respire.

Here's a lovely breathing practice of affirmations you can use all day long. It's a fantastic breathing exercise to teach to others, that I believe everyone should learn and practice. This is from the book *Deep Breathing* by Elma N. Forshey:

• (Inhale) I breathe in Christ.

(Exhale) and breathe frustration away;

• (Inhale) I breathe in Christ.

(Exhale) and breathe out anger;

• In God I breathe

(Inhale) and push the air out.

• (Inhale) My whole being reacts to this.

(Exhale) I'm refreshed, resurrected and reborn.

• (Inhale) I am ready to continue all over again!

At each meeting, we read "we are self-supporting by our efforts." What I have found is that you have to be self-supporting... You have to be self-sufficient. You need to shift the self-defeating, misguided thought that fills your mind.

God makes no garbage! Supported by anonymity.

Individuals (most, if not all, of them) join the rooms that hate themselves, the world, life, and God. They think they're special, smarter than anyone else, or at least that's what I've learned all along with my sobriety. You have to stick around long enough to know that you are not the centre of the universe, that God is in control and that everything is in divine order. I must emphasize the positive, delete the negative, don't mess with Mr In-between!

I found I needed to protect my mind. I needed to delete those mantras that were playing through my head endlessly. "I'm not good enough, I'm broken, I'm dumb, No one will understand the stuff that happened to me," in the beginning, went through my mind all day. Slowly but gradually, we start experiencing suffering from others at meetings and remember it's the same as ours.

We need to be flexible enough to change the mantras in our minds which run 24/7.

Jack Canfield states that "the removal of one negative thought or opinion includes 100 positive statements. Affirm yourself, learn to praise yourself... it's essential to start believing you're a child of God and as the poster says, 'God doesn't make waste.'"

Write down your affirmations. Not just what you believe now, but what you hope to believe in someday. Like, I thought I was stupid. To me, my teachers, my grades and my parents emphasized that often enough. One of my first sentences was: "I'm smart." Did I believe it? No. But just say it enough, and it's going to become your reality. Create a list that's the opposite of what you're telling yourself. I'm adding some examples to use here:

DO ALCOHOL AFFIRMATIONS WORK?

Will affirmations work for alcohol withdrawal?

The other day, I got a message from someone who said, "Affirmations are a bunch of bollocks. They're not working."

I will admit you are right! Affirmations don't work unless you let them work. When you think they're not working-then, they're not working.

They work for me because my antidote to my negativity is affirmations.

I have a whole lot of affirmations that I use when I have negative feelings. Ones that I can continuously say myself. I may brainwash my own emotions into thinking something else.

Self-talk: Whether we like it or not, what we say ourselves in our minds is the greatest control in our lives. You may give yourself negative self-talk or have positive self-talk. It all depends on you.

You have the opportunity to sit down and think carefully about the phrases you use-the words you use. Words are powerful.

The sentences you always say to yourself are so strong. They can change the course of your life, not just long-term-but in the short-term too. When I embarked on this journey I had a lot of affirmations that I used when I first started drinking.

I used to wake up early in the morning, and the first thing I'd do was drink my coffee.

Then I would sit down with a cup of tea and pull out a pad I-it was a legal pad of form A4.

I'd write out my twenty affirmations, and I'd say them to myself as I wrote them down.

I'd do the same in the evening.

I had a list of those affirmations in my wallet, in a plastic envelope, and I would pull them out when I felt crap about myself, crap about my decision to stop drinking, or whatever.

I'd just throw the list of affirmations down.

One of the affirmations was-

- I'm not mourning alcohol's death.

- Alcohol is my enemy, and I am not going to grieve.

- I no longer need it, and so I no longer use it.

I have completely different affirmations that I now use for myself.

Those claims have evolved from "alcohol is my enemy" to "alcohol is a bastard."

The terminology I used has got worse and worse.

Nobody else will hear those things. No-one else will see them. So, you can use anything that you want. You've got your chance to do this. When I was doing it myself, this played in my head, I repeated them over and over.

You're brainwashed by all of the propaganda going on there, by your friends, by all your peers – you 're going to be brainwashed by yourself as well.

As I said, you're often affected by the things you speak to yourself in your head over and over.

If you want to tell yourself good things; or if you want to say negative things about yourself, both work equally well.

When you want to be negative and make negative comments regularly, that's what's going to happen in your life.

Then, sadly, if you add misery into your life, that's essentially what you'll have. Negativity all around. And you might be adding positivity as well.

Affirmations are just good brainwashing lines carefully organized, so you sit down and think for yourself. You want to incorporate that into your own life.

You need to constantly remind yourself that you are a self-confident person; if that is what you want to get into life, if you want self-confidence.

To make these affirmations successful, they have to be positive

They have to be about something unique that you want in your life.

They have to be personalized. So, they have to be around you.

They have to be written in the present moment, and you're writing them as if you've done the thing before, as though you're living in the present. Now, you're doing it. You do what you want to do with your career.

If you want to self-direct your behavior, this is just another tool to use.

Like any tool, if you use it in the wrong way, or you don't think it will work-it won't work. Ultimately, this is it. This is what this channel is about. My theory is all about action, which is self-directed. The more that you can direct your actions, the more that you have power over yourself.

The more you admit to yourself – "I might be an addict," or "I am vulnerable to the drug epidemic" – the more treatment you can accept.

When you're forcing yourself into a box and marking yourself in various cul-de-sacs, the less power you have over yourself.

Affirmations are just one way of giving power to you. When you want these things to be used then use them. If you don't want to use them, then it's no skin off my nose. They work for me; but might not work for everyone.

My hypothesis of why this doesn't work for certain is that

people don't believe they work.

Have you ever seen someone doing a bungee jump?

Not that I'd ever be doing a bungee jump, that's not my thing, but if someone was standing on the edge of the platform there, look down behind them into the gorge. They have a piece of elastic attached to their bottom. Everybody else says to them, "You're going to be okay."

There is always someone there; there are people who are going to go "no worries" and just dive off. Face the threats as they come and take the consequences.

There will always be somebody there who is going to go – "I can't do it, I can't do it, I can't do it, I don't want to do it" No matter how they ended up on the edge of the precipice.

They've come too far at that moment to get themselves into the harness, they've got the elastic wrapped around their feet... but they don't. They think about it to themselves.

That is an assumption. It is the same thing. Whether it's positive or negative, it is self-talk.

You can think about it to yourself. So, if you think you can talk about something to yourself, then why can't you believe you can talk about something to yourself.

That's exactly what it is.

This label given to this is affirmation, but you can name it whatever you want. Positive self-discussion is perhaps a better way

256

to do this, but I prefer reinforcement because it means it is organized. It's the standardized expression you're using; you're repeating yourself over and over before you understand it. Before you are a member of it.

That's what my twenty affirmations were like.

So many times I've written these, morning and night. I was listening to them as I was composing them. Then I went through them again after I had written them down, and said them out loud again. Tonight I did the same thing. Any time I had to make my comments, I would do it, I had them committed to memory.

I could write those affirmations word by word at the end of a month, without looking at what I had written before. They stuck in my mind.

If you have a desire or a symptom, then you can take out a statement that says;

"I'm no Drinker anymore. Alcohol is a sick brute. I will never put the stuff back in my mouth again." This is what affirmations do. They're just sentences you're using for your gain that's what they're if you want them to be used-use them.

Suppose you don't want them to be used- don't use them. When you think they don't work, then they won't work.

The distinction between mild or social alcohol use and drinking disorder is thin and sometimes subtle. But when you find that you need alcohol to relax your senses, when you feel down or depressed, when a drink becomes a necessity, and when you no longer have control of what's going on in your life, it's time to deal with the issue and do whatever it takes to heal yourself.

In this situation, healing is way more than just detoxifying the body. You have lost your sense of balance somewhere along the way, and your self-esteem along with it. It will take time and commitment to win it back and find peace and joy in life again, but you've got what it takes to do it!

You have been neglecting yourself for far too long and now is the time to put an end to this and make a fresh start. This album has been designed to support you all the way and to help you start enjoying yourself again, to stop your mind from wandering and giving in to the negative thoughts that keep you from taking a better, healing course.

What to Look for

Affirmations are a simple but powerful instrument that will:

- Help you identify your goal and stay motivated to start again. You're about to stop looking for a way to numb your senses and wander away, trying to avoid your question. The song will help you face it and remain focused on your mission of liberating yourself from alcohol abuse – instead of giving in to the temptation to drink; you'll concentrate on overcoming it and taking meaningful steps to rebuild your life again.

- Make yourself more respected, and increase your self-confidence. This is probably the most important feature of this album. You can forgive yourself and encourage yourself to have a good life filled with love and happiness by changing the way you see yourself and helping you rediscover your worth. You will be motivated to rebuild your body and mind and start treating yourself with love and care, avoiding something that does not help your physical and emotional health.

- Motivate you to rebuild your relationships and strengthen your dream of a better future awaiting you. Holding a strong vision of a bright and prosperous future in your mind is a powerful motivator that will encourage you to work harder, remain strong day after day, and take action to fix your personal and professional ties. You will find that each small move is a small win for you, and this string of wins will motivate you to continue to overcome the desire until it is a matter of the past.

CREATING POSITIVE AFFIRMATIONS

A t first, glance, producing affirmations can seem like a 'no-brainer.' But wait... there is a right and a wrong way to build them like any other ability in life.

Generating affirmations the wrong way would be a waste of time. Doing them the wrong way will frustrate others, interfere with your success and may end up with you becoming one of the masses saying "Affirmations aren't working!" Yet affirmations DO work, and they should work for you. Here, you'll find out how to make the highest quality affirmations.

And instead of designing them the wrong way or even worse — end up programming yourself in harmful and divisive ways, follow the guidelines below!

HOW TO MAKE AFFIRMATIONS

Here are the nuts and bolts of making affirmations – fantastic shift in life, brain reprogramming, affirmations.

1. Determine the 'sound' that your assertions should have.

There are three voices which can be used:

❖ First Individual
❖ Second Individual
❖ Third Individual

- Affirmations by the first person look like this:

  - ➤ "I am ..."
  - ➤ "I am a resounding success."
  - ➤ "I'm feeling super positive."

- Affirmations from the second person look like this:

  - ➤ "You are ..."
  - ➤ "You're a great guy."
  - ➤ "You're pretty sure."

- Affirmations by a third party look like this:

  - ➤ "He's just ..."
  - ➤ "He's a great guy."
  - ➤ "He's incredibly positive."
  - ➤ Third-person affirmations are fascinating because you may include your name in the sentence-like this:

  "Mary is always full of excitement."

I encourage you to use all three if you make affirmations.

2. Consider the duration of your affirmation:

They should be short and simple. The explanation is that you send a message to your subconscious, rather than your conscious mind. The more complicated the statement, the more likely your subconscious mind won't accept the message. For example:

  - "I enjoy working out."
  - "I am happy forever."
  - "I am cool."

3. Setting the tone

Your affirmations should always be solid and productive. Words that indicate you can't lose should appear in your statements of affirmation. Try to avoid:

- "I am going to try ......"
- "I could ..."
- "Maybe I'll ......"
- "I am probably going to ..."

See how those sentences are pushing you ...

- "I am going to try to stop smoking."
- "I should feel comfortable."
- "I could get rich."
- "I am going to lose weight."

You can repeat these claims until you're blue in the face and you're going to experience no change whatsoever in your life — None. Zip.

Your subconscious mind is going to give you exactly what you mean. If you don't mean it, you won't get it.

Repeating an affirmation will insert the assertion into your subconscious mind, again and again – finally, it becomes your reality. Be very mindful about what you think and say, what you say is what you are going to be manifesting.

You're going to become whatever you think.

Positive or negative affirmations set the stage. C ranking affirmations require an optimistic twist.

It's best to say "I'm comfortable and happy now" instead of "I don't have any stress." The "I don't have any stress" problem is the negativity. You have to think about what "no stress" means when you put that little word in there. It will cause your mind to concentrate on stress with the possible outcome of generating MORE stress.

If someone was trying to tell you not to worry about the red-faced monkey, what will happen? Immediately, you think of a red-faced monkey!

Creating affirmations involves focusing on what you want and not on what you don't want.

4. Affirmations are time-sensitive.

Hold the affirmations in the present tense. Consider-

• "My strength is completely overflowing now."

or

• "My strength will burst exponentially in three months."

A well-thought-out affirmation does not reflect your present reality. Why use affirmations to say something that is part of your character already?

Affirmations aim to bring about transformative change by turning thought into physical/mental/emotional reality... a reality that currently does not exist in your life. Whatever your aim is – be sure of that – expertly crafted with the right affirmations, you WILL alter.

You'll experience sweeping success!

POPULAR AFFIRMATIONS IN RECOVERY

An affirmation may be whatever you want it to be, but some of the most common ones people make use of in recovery include:

- One at a time
- Do not take the first drink
- If you work it, it works
- Let go, and let Christ
- I came to believe
- Only today
- Let your blessings count
- Half steps didn't help us
- Easy does it, but do it
- If I think I won't drink if I drink, I can't think
- To make it, fake it.

TIPS FOR USING POSITIVE AFFIRMATIONS

- Never use the term "should" in affirmation
- Do use the present tense when making your affirmations, "I am more productive" and not "I want to be more productive."
- Use positive affirmations to combat any daily negative thinking you have – for example, if you think about repeating regularly, you could use the phrase "I am sober and solid."
- It is recommended that you focus on only a few affirmations instead of making too many of them.
- You have to feel words as you're using them.
- Meditating on your affirmations can be very helpful you can use them as a form of mantra.
- Repeat your sentences as soon as you wake up and repeat them when you have time all day long.
- You don't have to spend money on pricey apps to appreciate the power of affirmations – there's a lot of stuff out there to

get you to fork out some money (paying for affirmations doesn't make things any better).

SPECIFIC AFFIRMATIONS TO COMBAT ALCOHOL ABUSE

It is important to get medical support and help if you are dealing with substance addiction. We've mentioned some encouraging suggestions here that you can use to help you give up alcohol dependency on your journey. You may also write your affirmations about yourself and your circumstances.

Saying good things about yourself prepares the brain for improvement. Studies show that making positive changes is easier through the use of positive affirmations. Using constructive affirmations affects your neuroplasticity or the psychology of redirecting the brain to new thought patterns.

- You are using informal, first-person affirmations. As you tell these, you should feel your own goals and sense of duty.
- Only using optimistic terms. Remove negative words such as "I don't" or "I cannot."
- Consider your affirmations perfect for any difficulties or concerns in your life. You may make them restorative, or about relationships, or any other attributes that you want to focus on.
- I am using these daily. The goal is to get them ingrained into your consciousness.
- Hold simple affirmations. You want to pick and focus on one particular subject. Stop abstract, ambiguous terms.

The distinction between mild or social alcohol use and drinking disorder is thin and sometimes invisible. So when you find that you need alcohol to dull your senses, when you feel down or depressed, when a drink becomes a necessity, and when you no longer have control of what's going on in your life, it's time to deal with the issue and do whatever it takes to heal yourself.

Meditating means sitting. Positive affirmations for the treatment of addiction can be made by sitting down, putting on the headphones and finding a comfortable place to sit or lay down. The purpose is to decide the time to spend and then to be still and still deliberately. Reflect on your breathing and the affirmation tone. Focus profoundly upon the terms. Some people imagine every word as they hear it, putting them in the minds-eye on a virtual projector. The affirmations begin to help you slow your thinking to a steady, and healthy pace.

By safe, we mean that if you are actually in the flow of events, your synapses and neurology will be influenced positively. If you take in affirmations, you essentially swap what might be negative thinking trains for constructive, flowing and purposeful thoughts that will benefit you.

Words are words, and they act as instruments to suit the values you aspire to. With such optimistic affirmations for addiction rehabilitation, you can help your body heal itself and don't kid yourself that easy. Use such affirmations if you're hurt to help put your thoughts and decisions back into line with universal values that promote alignment of physical, mental, and emotional well-being.

266

Present Tense

- I am free of alcohol addiction
- I'm glad to know who I am
- I find peace inside of me
- I took my life into my own hands
- I take care of my physique
- People in my life support me
- I don't need alcohol to be content with myself and in peace
- I can handle anything that comes my way
- I can stay in control
- I surround myself with individuals that value me

Future Tense

- I am letting go of my alcohol addiction
- With each passing day, I become soberer and soberer
- I'll take care of my life
- I'll forgive myself for everything that I did
- I'm about to start fresh, alcohol-free life
- I profoundly respect and love myself
- I became a powerful person who has good behaviors
- I'll be taking care of my life
- I turn myself into one happy and peaceful human
- I'll spend my time with positive individuals, supporting individuals

Natural Tense

- Keeping away from the alcohol naturally appeals to me
- I deserve everything wonderful that life has to offer
- People consider me a good, happy and safe person
- With each day my life gets better
- I deserve a life free of alcohol addiction
- My life's packed with love and joy
- My interaction with people is curative

- People see me as someone who successfully over alcohol addiction
- Restoring my body and my soul

Your assumptions are supposed to mean something for you and they should be appropriate for your path. Don't wake up in the morning and tell yourself that you need to be good, that kind of pressure isn't needed. Instead, tell yourself you'll be happier, and you'll keep doing your best.

Make your self-affirmations a morning routine and you'll start to believe what you're telling yourself before you know it. Ultimately, you must always recall your self-affirmations to help you overcome any challenges that may occur during your rehabilitation.

Strong affirmations may benefit individuals who want to change things in their lives. They are sentences that are repeated in the present tense to themselves with trust to help the brain recognize and trigger a change in behavior.

The point of affirmations is not about changing who we are, but simply about how we feel about ourselves. We need to find out what applies to us as such. For some of us, positivity would succeed, while indifference could turn out to be the best course of action for others. For a few days or a few weeks, you could consider trying each approach. This will give you an idea of what strategy will work best for you. With that in mind, the solution you agreed on will move forward.

Affirmations are rarely a bad thing. There's nothing inherently wrong with telling ourselves we don't give ourselves enough credit. That said, we cannot make unbelievable statements. And if we choose positivity or negativity, we have to take the time to start believing the things we say. Otherwise, by setting ourselves unrealistic goals, we can do more damage than good. But if we keep our goals modest and seek to take action that supports our claims, we'll be in a good position. This has worked for others, and it will work for us most assuredly. We just need to give it a chance.

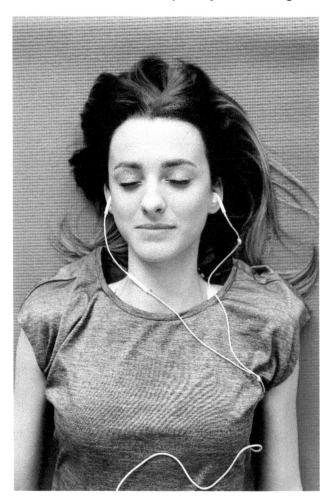

CONCLUSION

Alcoholism is when, given its detrimental effects, one can no longer regulate your alcohol consumption, compulsively misuse alcohol, and/or suffer mental distress while not drinking.

To quit drinking, using hypnosis is a realistic choice for those who want to change their lives.

Alcoholism is an illness that causes millions of deaths each year. Thousands of people around the world are succumbing to the consequences and every day suffering from alcohol poisoning. More than 15 million people are estimated to be dealing with alcoholism in the USA alone. The numbers are very troubling.

For decades now, people have viewed hypnosis as an effective treatment choice for substance use disorders. We also know that hypnosis can motivate abusers to give up alcohol as a result of clinical research, and can even avoid relapses.

Why are people addicted to alcohol? What makes men and women worldwide drink into oblivion?

Alcohol functions as a central nervous system depressant which means alcohol intake reduces normal brain function. Through the activity of a neurotransmitter called GABA (or gamma-aminobutyric acid), alcohol helps to slow the brain. On top of this, alcohol also interacts with natural endorphin production.

How GABA Changes Your Brain

GABA is the neurotransmitter responsible for your brain's inhibitions which makes it non-specific. The neurotransmitter does not reach a particular part of the brain when the GABA signals are increased but affects all of it instead. This is why people who drink heavily show symptoms such as poor motor control (have difficulty walking), loss of memory, impaired verbal skills (slurred speech), or even loss of consciousness.

Nonetheless, here's the crunch. Your body can adapt to its environment, and the brain is possibly the first to adapt to every scenario. When you drink alcohol regularly, the brain can adjust to tolerate GABA 's inhibitory effects by increasing the stimulating effects of other neurotransmitters such as glutamate.

There are opposing effects of glutamate and GABA. Your body relies on glutamate to transmit signals at an increased rate when the brain needs to. Yet to survive GABA's inhibitive effects, the body is changing to produce more glutamate.

As a result, you grow a tolerance for alcohol. Alcohol induces the same effects in your body, but you're more immune to its inhibitory effects. And, to get into the same state of drunkenness, you need to drink more.

Your body adjusting to GABA is the start of a vicious tolerance circle – increased drinking – greater tolerance – even more drinking, and so on. Finally, the vicious cycle contributes to dependency and addiction.

The Dark Side of Alcohol Tolerance

And if you thought this was the story's ending, you were mistaken. The brain adapts to withstand GABA's inhibitive effects by increasing glutamate production. But when this happens, when you stop drinking, you will start having withdrawal symptoms such as tremors (usually in the hands), hallucinations, and even convulsions.

That is because your brain is over-stimulated now. The brain has evolved to send further signals to surmount GABA's inhibitive effects and will continue to do so even though you quit drinking for a while.

If you've hit that level, it's fair to say you're into alcohol addiction. It would be very difficult to leave, and it may be risky to stop drinking altogether.

How Alcohol Interferes with Endorphins

Alcohol helps the body release more endorphins. Endorphins are naturally occurring substances in your body that act as neurotransmitters and send signals from one neuron to another. Your body has more than 20 forms of endorphins, and beta-endorphins have greater effects than cocaine or even morphine.

By now you've already read of dopamine, oxytocin, and

serotonin. Okay, these molecules are endorphins, and they are involved in many processes, ranging from producing euphoria and calming feelings to supporting women during conception.

Recent studies indicate that alcohol does affect the function of the human brain by inducing the release of endorphins. It is particularly noticeable in those who began to drink alcohol as adolescents.

And you can feel how alcohol contributes to endorphin release.

- You feel comfortable as soon as you have a drink or you might even be feeling euphoric.

- Your inhibitions are dropping-along with your other brain functions-making you feel confident and capable.

- Not only are your inhibitions reduced, but the logical part of your brain is impaired, and you are susceptible to make decisions that have potentially negative or dangerous consequences.

- Alcohol is relaxing your mind and body, so you can feel like getting a couple before you go to bed. It can cause you to believe you are unable to sleep without alcohol consumption, leading to the development of mental barriers that hamper your attempts to give up booze.

If you enjoyed this book, please let me know your thoughts by leaving a short review on Audible. Thank you!

QUIT SMOKING HYPNOSIS

Guided Sleep Meditation to Overcome Nicotine Addiction, Reduce Stress and Get Smoke-Free in 30 Days with Hypnosis and Positive Affirmations + Stop Smoking Challenge!

By Elliott J. Power

Thanks again for choosing this book, make sure to leave a short review on Audible if you enjoy it. I'd really love to hear your thoughts.

INTRODUCTION

Quitting smoking can be very challenging. However, it is one of the best things you can do. Smoking is a dangerous and deadly habit. It's the number one cause of cancer. It also raises the risk of heart attacks, lung disease, strokes and other health problems including cataracts and bone fractures.

If patches, gum chewing, nicotine lozenges, counselling and other forms of smoking cessation have not helped you quit the habit, don't give up. Ask the doctor if hypnosis is an alternative. Some studies have shown that hypnosis can help some people stop smoking.

What is Hypnosis?

Hypnosis is described as an altered state of consciousness where you seem to be asleep or in a trance. Clinical hypnosis can be used to treat some psychological or physical conditions. It's also used to help patients control pain. It's used in a wide variety of other conditions such as weight problems, speech disorders and problems with addictions.

There is a debate on how the hypnosis works. Many people believe you relax and focus more while you're hypnotized, so they're more likely to listen to suggestions — like giving up smoking, for example.

While, during hypnosis, you do appear to be in a trance, you are not unconscious. You're still conscious of your surroundings, and despite what many stage performers may say during an entertainment show — you cannot be forced to do anything against your will.

However, brain tests performed on patients during hypnotism sessions revealed a high degree of neurological activity.

Hypnosis for Smokers

During smoking cessation hypnosis, a patient is often asked to imagine negative smoking outcomes. The hypnotherapist may say, for example, that cigarette smoke smells like truck exhaust, or that smoking may leave the patient's mouth feeling extremely parched.

Spiegel's method is a common technique of hypnosis of smoking cessation, which focuses on three main ideas:

- You need your body to live

- Smoking poisons the body

- You should respect and protect your body (to the extent you'd like to live)

The hypnotherapist advises the smoker to use self-hypnosis, and then tells him or her to reiterate these affirmations if there is a need to smoke.

Does Hypnosis Work?

Hypnosis, in general, doesn't work for everyone. About one in every four people cannot be hypnotized. When successful, the depth of the hypnosis can differ from person to person.

How well the hypnosis works to help people stop smoking depends on who you ask. Results for the study have been mixed. A systematic analysis of scientific research in 2010 revealed that there wasn't adequate evidence to justify the use of hypnosis. Another study released in 2012 said the use of hypnosis offers a potential benefit. The American Cancer Society states in exploring alternative strategies for stopping smoking on its website that while controlled studies have not proven the efficacy of hypnosis, there is anecdotal evidence that certain people have been helped.

Hypnosis is not an approved treatment by the American Medical Association (AMA), despite some websites and promotional materials that suggest otherwise. The organization 's position on using hypnosis is not official. In 1987 the AMA rescinded a consensus statement related to the use of the technique for medical and psychological purposes.

Experts who have researched hypnosis say further, well-conducted research is required to establish if hypnosis helps smokers quit the habit for good, however, adds that hypnosis remains a promising solution and has several other benefits. The best way to quit, however, may be to combine multiple strategies.

How to Find a Hypnotherapist

Ask your healthcare professional to recommend a successful hypnotherapist if you want to try hypnosis to help you stop smoking.

Below are some tips to find a professional hypnotherapist:

- Ensure they are licensed, qualified and certified. Hypnosis for smoking cessation and other medical reasons should only be done by someone with a current license in a field of health care, such as psychiatry, medicine, psychology, or nursing.

- Ask any difficult questions. Ask about the professional training. Also, the American Society for Clinical Hypnosis suggests asking: "Can this practitioner help me without hypnosis? "If the answer is no, look elsewhere then.

- Beware of the claims or promises that are too good to be true. Hypnosis doesn't work for everyone.

It's never too late to stop smoking. Doing so has immediate benefits for health. If you stop smoking before you turn 50, you will cut the risk of dying in the next fifteen years compared to those who keep lighting up.

We have all heard about hypnosis. We've seen the magical practitioners on the adverts promising to liberate us forever from addiction. We've successfully seen Chandler Bing quit smoking just by falling asleep on some tapes calling him strong and confident.

But most of us aren't quite sure what hypnosis is. Where the idea originated from? Is it anything to do with snake-charming? Most importantly: Can it help break a habit of smoking?

I looked into the subject of hypnosis a little deeper, so I can help my readers to distinguish reality from fiction.

The Origins of Hypnosis

In the early 20th century, Sigmund Freud, the founding father of psychoanalysis, brought hypnosis back into the limelight. He wasn't the first to bring up the idea. He was a figurehead also for the role played by hypnosis in modern psychology and medicine.

Freud used hypnosis to help his patients access their unconscious mind to desires and fears. In conversation with the psychoanalyst, patients will enter a trance-like state and allow their deepest feelings to surface. Freud theorized that this would allow them to free up crippling emotions and recover from their anxiety, or hysteria.

Freud was a very bad hypnotist (and smoked like a chimney). Nevertheless, modern health care practitioners have considered

Freud 's theories on hypnosis useful. This is because the hypnosis provides a changed state of consciousness. This will allow the subconscious mind to be accessed. The individual will then be able to channel and resolve underlying desires and fears to help them work towards their objectives.

How Hypnosis Works

Experts on hypnosis also provide people with goals to boost their health. Quitting smoking is a common health goal. We all know the advantages of being a non-smoker: healthy skin, higher life expectancy and a greatly reduced risk of lung cancer or heart attack.

You're likely to have some misgivings about the idea of hypnosis and how it works to quit smoking. The thought of getting a stranger induced into a trance is very compelling. You think of this as something entertainers like David Blaine might do to embarrass members of the audience at magic shows.

If you're considering hypnotherapy, I'm here to tell you that Derren Brown won't rock up and trick you into drinking a bottle of vinegar. The goal of professional hypnotherapists is not to make you do things that you don't want. Nevertheless, research shows that hypnosis does not work unless there are existing intentions for the subject to achieve something.

Hypnosis also involves amplifying current wishes-including the need to stop smoking!

So, what would happen during a session of hypnotherapy?

There are many ways to induce hypnosis, none of which includes swinging a watch in front of your eyes (this is a Hollywood myth). The quick movement would be distracting. Hypnosis revolves around concentration.

Hypnotic induction techniques are meant to relax the conscious mind and achieve a trance-like state. The therapists use suggestion and word combinations to have this effect on clients. Hypnotic induction may take place within guided sessions or by using pre-recorded tapes (self-hypnosis).

Entering into a hypnotic trance is not the same as sleeping. It's a very deep state of altered consciousness. Scans have shown that during hypnosis, people generally experience greater brain activity. This increased brain activity is intended to allow an individual to concentrate on their specific goal.

Studies have proposed that some people frequently enter trance-like states. Have you ever been concentrating on a project that you have forgotten lunch? This intense concentration is known as a spontaneous trance, whereas the induction of a hypnotic trance is deeper.

The therapists introduce clients to 'hypnotic suggestions' until they enter a trance. These are statements which promote goals of control, confidence and a smoking-free life.

Often, the client is asked to visualize some things. As a non-smoker, those might be optimistic aspects of a future. They may also be uncomfortable sensations related to current smoking habits.

For these activities, therapists should follow standardized scripts. But sessions on hypnosis can differ a great deal. Hypnosis does not share the same base of evidence as other smoking addictions treatments. This means that approaches like cognitive-behavioral therapy do not have the same proven guidelines.

HYPNOSIS TO QUIT SMOKING – HOW EFFECTIVE IS IT?

Using hypnosis to stop smoking might sound like wishful thinking. However, can you stop smoking for good with the aid of hypnotherapy? In this part of the book, we will discuss the effects on smoking using hypnotherapy, to see whether it brings anything new to the table or not.

The Dangers of Smoking

Smoking causes up to seven million deaths a year, so quitting should be your main priority.

Ditching smoking can be a real challenge. Smoking is a toxic habit that can lead to cancer and death. Although 1.1 billion people around the world are smokers, according to the World Health Organization (WHO). Sadly, many of these smokers come from low- or middle-income countries, and they are suffering from diseases related to tobacco.

The WHO finds the tobacco crisis one of the world's most important challenges to public health. Tobacco consumption is responsible for up to seven million deaths per year. Unfortunately, as many as half of the people who use tobacco die from it.

While most people find it difficult to stop smoking, there are some factors that can help. Lozenges, nicotine patches, and chewing gum will help you conquer your addiction.

However, if you've tried any of these approaches without any success, you don't have to worry. There is still something you can try.

Hypnosis for Smoking

Hypnotherapy is great for helping you break bad habits and deal with stress. Although hypnotherapy is used in a number of ways, it is especially good to relax the mind and help you overcome the risk of relapse.

The History of Hypnosis as a Treatment for Smoking

In the 1950s psychologists started using hypnotherapy as an aid to traditional therapy for psychological care. Back in 1958, hypnotherapy was accepted as a therapeutic treatment by the American Psychological Association (APA) and the American Medical Association (AMA).

Hypnotherapy was first used by Dr Herbert Spiegel to help people stop smoking and was first published in 1970. His treatment technique is well recognized and is still used to this day as the

"Spiegel Method."

Modern hypnotherapists use suggestions to encourage smokers to replace tobacco and cigarette smoke with unpleasant feelings that help smokers quit. The hypnotherapists can also improve the ability of smokers to cope with their symptoms of nicotine withdrawal and reduce their urge to smoke.

Hypnosis to Quit Smoking – What Does Science Say?

Hypnosis has always been a controversial topic. People are sceptical about the advantages of hypnotherapy because this alternative medicine branch has been misrepresented for decades in movies and other forms of media. Some people believe that hypnotherapy is nothing but stage magic, while others believe that under the influence of hypnosis, they become more susceptible to suggestion.

However, there are many studies based on the efficacy of the smoking hypnosis. Here are their findings:

1993 Study

A 1993 study looked at the effectiveness of hypnotherapy for smoking cessation. The interesting thing about this study, after a single hypnosis session, is that it studied the effects of hypnotherapy for smokers.

226 Smokers received a single session of hypnosis involving self-hypnosis. Two years after the report, the researchers contacted the smokers to follow up on their findings. This research estimated

as a positive outcome only the complete abstinence from smoking.

A week after the hypnosis session, 52 percent of the people who participated in this study abstained from smoking. Over two years, 23 percent of participants maintained their abstinence. Curiously, the study showed that those who lived with a partner were more likely to abstain from smoking than those who did not.

The study found that hypnotherapy was mildly successful in helping people to stop smoking. The researchers discovered that hypnosis is preferable to voluntary efforts to give up smoking.

2008 Study

Research published in May 2008 aimed to determine whether hypnosis would be more effective in helping smokers quit than regular therapy. The randomized research recruited 286 smokers living in San Francisco. The smokers took part in two 60-minute counselling or hypnotherapy sessions, and after the study, they received three follow-up calls.

29 percent of those in the hypnotherapy group indicated abstaining from smoking after seven days into the study, compared to 23 percent in the counseling group.

Six months later, compared to 18 percent of the behavioral treatment group, 26 percent of people who were part of the hypnotherapy group indicated that they did not pick up the habit again.

One year after the study, 20 percent of the hypnotherapy group reported not smoking, compared to just 14 percent of the counselling group.

This research found hypnosis is more effective for long-term quit rates than traditional behavioral therapy.

2014 Study

Research published in 2017 looked at the effectiveness of smoking cessation hypnotherapy among students.

59 Students were randomly chosen to participate in the study. The researchers instructed the students in self-hypnosis techniques, and they asked the students to try it at home and keep a diary of how much they smoked for nine weeks.

The study found that after nine weeks of practicing hypnosis, 65.4 percent of students quit smoking. The study stated that the students smoked less after the program was introduced, and it suggests that hypnotherapy has therapeutic effectiveness in achieving a cessation of smoking among students.

What Makes Hypnosis Effective for Smokers?

So far, we have seen that part of the scientific community supports the use of hypnosis as an aid for those who want to give up smoking. But, why do smokers find hypnosis so effective?

A Different Mindset

Smokers will build a new attitude about cigarettes with the aid of hypnotherapy. The advice from hypnotherapists will make you see cigarettes for what they are.

One of the most common phrases you'll hear when someone tries to quit smoking is that they like to smoke. Well, to give in to your cravings is one thing, and it is another to say that you really like it.

With the aid of suggestions from the hypnotist, the mentality changes. Smoking can no longer be seen as something you want after the therapeutic intervention. You are going to see it as the threat it is. While some of the suggestions may make you nervous at first, they will not only help you stop smoking, but will also help you to conquer your cravings and possible relapses.

Helps You Help Yourself

Most people wrongly think only hypnotherapists can induce hypnosis. This is not true. You can learn to practice self-hypnosis with the aid of a guided therapy session, and help yourself overcome your addiction.

Some words and phrases might help your subconscious view cigarettes differently. Repeating these terms or phrases can help you fight the desire to light a cigarette, and can help you abstain from smoking in the future.

Complementary Method

One of the positive things about hypnotherapy is that to improve the chances of stopping smoking, you can combine it with other approaches. Not only this, hypnotherapy can also improve the effects of certain forms of smoking cessation, such as nicotine patches or chewing gum.

Hypnosis can allow the mind to conquer the addiction while the nicotine gum or patches can allow the body deal with the effects of nicotine withdrawal.

CHAPTER 1
TRYING TO QUIT SMOKING? HERE'S
HOW SELF-HYPNOSIS COULD HELP

W ant 2020 to be the year you quit smoking for good? According to research from the Change Incorporated Quit Cigarettes mission, more than half (56%) of smokers have tried to quit this month – and more than half (53%) admit they 're feeling anxious or nervous about it.

It's not easy to stop smoking. It can be very difficult indeed – but it is possible with the right approach and support. So, if you're still struggling, or have failed previous attempts to quit, maybe it's time to try a new approach?

Smokers are up to four times more likely to quit for good if they use a combination of a medical professional's smoking cessation treatments and support instead of trying to go 'cold turkey.'

Doctor-turned-TV hypnotherapist Aaron Calvert has partnered up with Change Incorporated to help smokers get to the right mindset to quit through self-hypnosis, guided breathing exercises, and mindfulness. Studies show, he points out that you are much more likely to be able to quit for good if you can stay smoke-free for 7 days.

"People who decided to quit smoking cigarettes should feel extremely proud of themselves, because the first thing they should know is that they're not alone," Calvert says. "There are loads of people around the globe planning to quit right now, and I hope the tips and tricks I share make it as easy as possible for people to get through those first 7 days."

Calvert here discusses how to use self-hypnosis to quit smoking, along with several other suggestions to help you keep track of it.

Quitting Through Self-hypnosis,

Self-hypnosis can be used to help you achieve significant changes in your life, such as stopping smoking. Choose your session time and place – make sure it's quiet enough so you won't be interrupted.

Lie down or sit down, and close your eyes. Take three deep, slow breaths and hold the third breath in for three seconds. Relax and sink back into the seat while you breathe out. Concentrate on your breathing, and let your thoughts float in and out as if connected to your breathing until your mind is clear.

Now count backwards from 10 to zero, counting each number as you breathe out and concentrating on a different part of your body, helping it to relax. I begin with my toes and work up to my head, however, you may find that you prefer to do it from your head down to your toes.

You'll be relaxed at this point, but just imagine yourself in a quiet place to help deepen that relaxation. I like using a beach; imagine the beach in as much detail as possible. Try to imagine a meadow or a garden anywhere you feel most comfortable with if you dislike beaches.

Now you're in that state of relaxation and concentration, you can give yourself a suggestion, feel more comfortable about quitting smoking, or imagine your justification for quitting vividly so that you feel more inspired to achieve your goal.

When it's time to wake up, just count yourself all the way back from zero to 10 and you'll find yourself wide awake, feeling refreshed and re-energized. When you need to be immediately awake and alert during your session for some reason, you should be able to wake up, and of course, be yourself. This is it! It's so easy to really start making positive changes in your life.

1. **Text three friends**

If you're tempted to smoke, try texting three friends and wait for their responses before you give in. The urge would have passed by the time they've all replied.

2. **Choose your support network wisely**

Tell your loved ones you are quitting, because they're not only going to support you, they're going to motivate you and provide advice to help you. Also, telling people forces you to be truthful, particularly early on in your journey, as you have someone else to respond to.

3. Have a plan of action

Having a plan right from the start means you are more likely to succeed.

4. Know your reason for quitting

It's vital, to be honest with yourself – why are you quitting? Is it to save money, enhance your health or the health of those around you, or is it simply to help you look younger or smell better? Whatever the reason, find it, write it down – and put it anywhere you would usually smoke, helping you remember why you're making this positive change.

5. Reward yourself

When you fall back into old habits, it's easy to be over-critical of yourself. Slipping up is normal — learn to accept it, and keep on trying to quit. It's equally important to pat yourself on the back when you succeed. Plan to reward yourself when you reach a milestone period of time without smoking — after the vital first seven days, for example, which is worth celebrating.

6. Stay away from triggers.

There will be some things in your daily routine that you connect with smoking. It may be a morning coffee, meeting with some friends or during your work break. Avoid your triggers or change your routine for the first few days.

7. **Try straw therapy**

If you are tempted to smoke, you can replace a cigarette with a straw. Cut down a household straw and use it as you would a cigarette. So much smoking is anchored to the hand-to-mouth action, feeling something in your hands and taking a deep breath. This 'straw therapy' can help your body psychologically to stop that craving feeling.

8. **Relax**

Stopping smoking can make you feel more depressed than usual, so make sure you take some extra time out to relax. If you're running, doing some yoga, or using self-hypnosis and relaxation exercises, it's crucial to make sure you stay on top of your game and stay motivated while you quit.

Can You Quit Smoking Through Hypnosis?

"It is all about choice," the man said, with the soothing voice. "If you are here for someone else's pleasure, you can hang around and have some fun, but more than likely you'll go out and smoke after."

I was sitting in the basement of the public library in Arlington, Massachusetts, with a motley group of about 20, we were all skeptical and desperate, with one major thing in common: We smelled like an ashtray.

Theoretically, we should have come together because we no longer wanted to smoke cigarettes. "I am here for health reasons," said one lady. "Cigarettes are too expensive," said an elderly man.

"I am at dental hygiene school," another attendee added. "We should be promoting health, but how can I advise anyone else to quit smoking if I am myself?"

These are positive reasons people would want to stop smoking. It is the same for me, plus vanity, and, the grim specter of an earlier grave. (When you're gone, you can't look good.) So, if I really wanted to stop, why was the only thing I could think of was how much I wanted to go out and smoke a cigarette?

Mark Hall, a qualified hypnotherapist and licensed social worker, knows only too well. He stopped smoking himself several years ago — he says he still recalls reaching for a phantom lighter that wasn't in his pocket — and he's been having these sessions for over twenty years, with the intention of inspiring others that they can do it themselves.

His hypnotherapy sessions usually cost around $150, or $95 with insurance coverage, but this event, funded by the Sanborn Foundation for the Treatment of Cancer, was close to my house and open to the public. In other words, there was no excuse not to go, except maybe a question that had terrified me as the meeting challenged me all week: What if it didn't work? Or, maybe even worse: What if it does? Then what the hell do I do? Smoking is such a big part of my daily life, ridiculous as it sounds, the thought of losing it is disturbing.

Hall asked, "Does anyone here feel like cigarettes are their best friend?" Telling us to clap our hands, then clap them again, leading this time with the opposite hand to one we'd been used to. Everything felt different. Throughout the room, the tone also changed noticeably. "The point," Hall said, "was that, by muscle memory, smoking is a habit that we all do as involuntarily as the way we choose to clap our hands."

People can undergo hypnosis to tackle all kinds of issues — from addictions like mine to emotional trauma. There's some evidence that it may be an effective tool in treating eating disorders, dentistry, and post-traumatic stress disorder, and dealing with birth pain. But there is still enough uncertainty about what it really is given its prevalence, often even among those who have already committed to it. I definitely had no idea what I was in for because I was sitting in my superlatively uncomfortable chair, ready for something, okay. Or maybe nothing.

Hypnotism is such an amorphous concept that when I asked a couple of practitioners what it is, they spend a great portion of the discussion telling me what it is not. Most of us are familiar with the hypnosis process from the well-known stage hypnotist, where guests are picked up from the audience of the nightclub to go through humiliation on stage. Or, if not, then smugly tossing a stopwatch in front of a patient's face from fictional depictions of a Freudian type. These are both major misconceptions; Hall explained as he preps his crowd for the descent into a state of enhanced relaxation.

"My hypnosis is a therapeutic tool and not entertainment," he said, starting to make us feel at ease. But, he joked, "If you told someone you're going to be here tonight, I'll advise you to go home and start clucking like a chicken."

The practice today typically traces its origins back to the 1840s, when Scottish surgeon James Braid built on the notion of what he called "nervous sleep" or, more precisely, "the induction of a state of abstraction or mental concentration in which, as in reverie or unconscious abstraction, the forces of the mind are so profoundly engrossed with a single concept or stream of thought to render the individual unconscious of, or indifferently conscious to, all other ideas, or trains of thought, or impressions."

But, according to the hypnotist and author Charles Tebbutts, confusing hypnosis with sleep (the term is derived from the Greek for sleep), is incorrect as expressed by his student C. Roy Hunter: Mastering Basic Techniques in his book The Art of Hypnosis. Hypnotism, "is in reality a natural state of mind, and is usually induced much more often in daily life than is artificially induced. We are in a natural hypnotic trance every time we get immersed in a novel or a motion picture," Tebetts wrote. Hunter argues that claiming that hypnosis is simply self-hypnosis is more accurate. The hypnotherapist, much like a physical trainer, merely helps the subject persuade themselves to do something they were already able to do, nudging them in the right direction.

Although there is a broad range of methods and types of hypnotism practiced today — something that further confuses our ability to understand it critically or to research it scientifically — one thing they seem to have in common is an emphasis on relaxation, concentration, harnessing a desire to improve within the person, and creating verbal and visual connections between emotions.

As explained by the American Association of Professional Hypnotherapists: "Hypnosis is just a condition of relaxed concentration. It's a natural state. -- each of us usually enters such a state — sometimes called a trance state — at least twice a day: once when we fall asleep, and once when we wake up."

Hypnotherapists claim they make this cycle simpler, but without the sleeping part. Joseph P. Green and Steven Jay Lynn reviewed 56 studies on the outcomes of smoking cessation hypnosis in a 2000 study for the International Journal of Clinical and Experimental Hypnosis. Although it has usually been shown to be a better choice than no therapy at all, several studies combine hypnosis with other therapeutic approaches, making it difficult to isolate its effects.

It is rare that people try to stop smoking by hypnosis alone, so no two practices are the same, which explains why it is difficult to know if it works.

Moshe Torem, a psychology professor at Northeast Ohio Medical University and the president of the American Society of Clinical Hypnosis, one of many such professional organizations around the country, explained to me the components of the typical hypnotherapist process.

"Hypnosis is a different state of mind coupled with four main characteristics," he said. First is a "highly focused attention on something." It could be a problem that you have, or a problem that you want to address. Second, the subject disassociates themselves from the immediate physical environment. "In the middle of a Boston winter, you focus on the beach in Florida," he said, completely predicting my particular winter-addled frame of mind. "You're going there with your head, instead of driving, and you're completely focused on the beach."

Maybe a nice place to smoke a cigarette.

The third element is that of suggestibility. The person is more receptive to suggestions that he or she has provided. Fourth is what he terms "involuntariness," which means that when you come out of hypnosis, you believe subjectively you have done nothing but that you have achieved everything. For example, you may know that you are being asked to raise your arm, but you feel as though it is being raised by some outside force. Which makes sense, because I am driven by similar subconscious impulses when I reach for a cigarette, particularly when I know I do not need it.

CHAPTER 2
HYPNOSIS TO QUIT SMOKING: DOES IT
WORK?

Most smokers get hooked on a habit they hate. This is true. The majority of smokers- an estimated 80%, will be happy to never smoke another cigarette again.

It makes sense too.

We all know smoking is detrimental to your health, moderate smokers felt a sore throat or breathing difficulty as they climb a flight of stairs, and there is the possibility of more serious health effects. (Tobacco is responsible for 7 million deaths per annum worldwide, according to the World Health Organization.)

There are plenty of other reasons to quit, not to mention: To save money, having healthy skin, for your kids, becoming more active, etc.

But if most smokers want to quit, have multiple reasons to quit, and realize just how dangerous cigarettes are to their health, what stops them from doing so?

The reason for that is clear. Nicotine addiction is deeply rooted in the subconscious mind. Stress, driving, mealtime, drinking (and

300

the list goes on) all subconsciously cause cigarette cravings.

But what if your head had a way of "shutting off" the voice? Or at least reframe the subconscious thoughts to think about smoking negatively?

Well, this is the promise of hypnotherapy to quit smoking.

The smoker can begin to untangle and silence the web of subconscious thoughts that hold the addiction in place with the aid of a hypnotherapist or through self-hypnosis.

The Mental Trap: Why Can't You Stop Smoking

Because of physical and mental addiction, nicotine is such a hard habit to kick.

Physical addiction-which can cause withdrawal symptoms - serves as a roadblock to quitting.

Nicotine withdrawal causes:

- Aches and pains

- Sore throat

- Nausea

- Irritability

- Headache

- Mental sluggishness

But although the symptoms of nicotine withdrawal are painful, something is happening at a deeper level which makes it so difficult to quit smoking.

Mental addiction. Our subconscious emotions sustain the nicotine addiction. After dinner, or when you get behind the wheel, the subconscious causes the urge for a cigarette ... It's the subconscious mind that causes a pang when you're under stress.

This mental struggle also explains why most smoking cessation aids are ineffective, such as nicotine replacement therapy. Only physical cravings are eliminated by NRT – but those subconscious thoughts, those mental urges that tell us to reach for a cigarette are still very much in place.

But overcoming nicotine addiction requires smokers to fight the head-on mental battle. Thanks to top-down processing, the battle rages in your subconscious.

What is processed by top-down? Suppose a smoker who wants to quit has a major presentation at work. She is definitely feeling stressed out. The need for a cigarette might then be triggered by stress. But from where does this trigger originate?

Top-down processing may be effective in understanding the phenomenon.

In a nutshell, all the sensory information we obtain is sent to the brain - smell, touch, sights, feelings. The raw sensory data is transferred to the brain, where it produces a conscious perception. The brain then shapes feelings and emotions and provides a response.

In other words, the mind receives the signal of stress, thinks about what is going on and then generates a response that is focused on those thoughts.

It is the process that makes it so difficult to stop smoking.

Subconscious thoughts influence our top-down responses. You may associate smoking as a stress reliever, for example, and therefore your normal response to stress might be to light up.

The trick to stopping smoking is to gain top-down control-suppressing the unconscious reinforcement response that holds the addiction in place.

How Hypnosis Can Help You Quit:

One theory of why hypnosis works for addiction to nicotine: It allows us the opportunity to reframe our top-down thoughts.

Once you encounter stimuli that can induce craving, the mind has connections already in place that affect the response. You feel stressed out. The stress triggers smoking thoughts as a stress reliever. And you have responded.

However, hypnosis helps you get to a state of mind where you change the mechanisms of negative thinking.

How? Well, you follow relaxation and breathing strategies during hypnosis to achieve a trance-like state. This state of mind is similar to daydreaming; you are conscious, but the mind is detached at the same time.

Your mind is much more open to suggestions in the trance-state.

It's disconnected from the critical, conscious mind – the part of the mind that is actively trying to remain a smoker.

Hence, a hypnotherapist will give you more constructive ideas to use. In other words, you are setting up roadblocks for the automatic, top-down mechanisms that keep the addiction in place. And when you experience a smoking trigger, the mind does not react automatically – it slows down to "listen" to this new information that you've received.

Reframing Your Subconscious Thoughts

Our subconscious thoughts are powerful and shape our perceptions. And when our subconscious tells us that this will work, we send the information back through top-down processing.

Hypnosis works in a similar fashion. We bring fresh, more detailed knowledge about smoking to our minds.

Hypnotic suggestions – those offered while in the state of trance – may concentrate on how habits are automatic reactions to thoughts, and how we have full control over our thoughts. Or you might be given ideas that rethink the smell of cigarette smoke, that is, it smells like burning plastic.

Additionally, one of the most common hypnosis techniques for smoking cessation is called the Spiegel's Method. One of the first psychiatrists to popularize therapeutic hypnotherapy, Herbert Spiegel was the author of "Trance and Treatment: Clinical Uses of Hypnosis."

Spiegel would provide three repeated suggestions in a hypnosis script during the sessions including:

- Smoking is poison

- You should love your body and protect it

- You need your body to live

Spiegel 's method did not focus on talking about stopping smoking. Actually, he theorized that making patients concentrate on respecting the body was key to changing destructive behavior .

Research Review: Stop Smoking with Hypnosis

We have touched on the hypnosis theory for stopping smoking. However, we haven't answered your question yet: Will hypnosis actually help you stop smoking?

The quick response is yes. Hypnosis has been found by some compelling studies to be an efficient tool to help you quit – with quit rates that easily beat more conventional methods.

Yet, like with any smoking cessation program, the consensus seems to be that you have to want the results. The best option is not hypnotherapy if:

• You feel like you should stop, but you don't really want to.

• You aren't ready to quit.

• You want to quit for someone else.

However, if you're ready, hypnosis can be an effective tool. A classic research on hypnosis explored the use of hypnotherapy across a variety of conditions. The study found that hypnotherapy needs an average of just six sessions of hypnotherapy to create a long-lasting improvement, whereas psychoanalysis takes 600.

It was seen that hypnosis was highly effective after six sessions 93% of participants, while the psychoanalysis group had a recovery rate of just 38%.

Several other studies have found evidence that hypnosis is a useful therapy for smoking cessation.

A scientific study at the American College of Chest Physicians conducted in 2007 compared hypnosis to nicotine replacement therapy. At 26 weeks, 50% of patients enrolled in the hypnotherapy group were still non-smokers, compared to only 15.78% in the nicotine replacement group. Patients of NRT and hypnotherapy have had a success rate of 50% at 26 weeks.

A study published in Psychological Reports in 1994 examined the effectiveness of hypnotherapy in combination with aversion therapy. In the research, a cessation program was undertaken by 93 male and 93 female participants, incorporating both approaches. About 90% of both groups abstained from smoking after three months.

A research published in the International Journal of Clinical and Experimental Hypnosis in 2001 examined the effectiveness of hypnosis and a quick smoking cessation protocol. The results: After 6 months, 39 of the 43 smokers who received treatment remained non-smokers.

306

A comprehensive meta-analysis reviewed more than 600 studies that examined various approaches for smoking cessation. The study has included more than 70,000 smokers. The study finds some convincing findings on hypnosis in general:

- Hypnosis was deemed two times more effective than self-help techniques, like quitting cold turkey or reading self-help books.

- Hypnosis was twice as effective as the nicotine gum replacement therapy

- Hypnosis was three times more effective than treatments by physicians involving more than counselling.

Are you ready to live a smoke-free life? Want to use hypnosis as an alternative for the therapy? You have many ways to use hypnosis to stop your cravings for smoking, all of which will help you curb your habit. The most popular of the three include:

- Private Hypnotherapy Sessions – You talk to a professional hypnotherapist directly. The hypnotherapist will ask you about your condition during a one-on-one session, which occurs over the phone, and then lead you through a hypnosis session.

- Recorded Sessions – Guided hypnosis sessions, typically available on a CD or as MP3s, offer a similar experience to private sessions. The main difference is the session is driven by a recording. You listen to the recording, following the steps to enter hypnosis.

- Self-hypnosis-Self-hypnosis appears to play a significant role in prevention of smoking. If you began with a private session, for example, you will possibly continue the therapy with self-hypnosis at home. In self-hypnosis, to enter the trance state, you undergo a hypnotic induction and then read from a hypnosis script to make suggestions to yourself. A quit smoking hypnosis script can also help.

CHAPTER 3
IMPROVE YOUR STATE OF MIND AND
FORM A HEALTHY MINDSET

W hen most people seek to become healthy, they just concentrate on physical features. They change their eating habits and follow a fitness routine. All truly great improvements to make, but the mental health of one is what sometimes gets ignored. When you want to be genuinely happy in life, both your physical and mental health needs to be in good form. If you are in a positive state of mind, you would be in a much better place to work in your daily life. It is especially important to be optimistic when you are facing challenges. Staying committed to a safe, active lifestyle is hard if you can't hold your head up in an upbeat space.

Here are ten tips that could just help you stay sunny and positive:

1. Accept Yourself for Who You Are.

This one is huge. A lot of people struggle with self-esteem and self-worth every day. We're bombarded with images all day long and running comments telling us how we are "supposed" to look and act. If you continually compare yourself to others it can be difficult to find value. Striving for changes is necessary, but you must also note that you can only do it for you, not for anyone else. You are you and that is pretty awesome.

You are never going to look like anyone else. What you'll ever look like is a better you. In this world nothing is more important than doing the best you can.

2. Eat Healthy.

This is obvious because it is true. If you eat nothing but processed foods, nutritionally void, you will be doing yourself a disservice. When you eat healthy, fresh, whole foods, your body will function better and so will your brain. The processed foods contain chemicals that have a detrimental effect on your brain. When you are always feeling nervous or stressed out, consider cutting out caffeine and foods containing significant quantities of salt and sugar.

Check out BodyRock Meal Plan for some very nice meal ideas that will keep your body and mind healthy! This plan contains more than just a meal planner, a diet guide AND a recipe book with over 70 offers!

3. Surround Yourself with Positive People.

Being around positive people, and expressing your aspirations and dreams, will boost your well-being. Make time to see friends and relatives. Take time to laugh. Have fun together. These people who love you can make you feel confidence and joy. It is so important to be appreciated for who you are.

If you have relationships that don't make you feel this way in your life, it may be time to re-examine whether they are worth keeping or not.

4. Appreciate the Little Things.

We are so busy that we can fail to consider the little stuff. Slow down, put all your electronics away. Breathe, then go for a walk. Take note of all you see. Take it in. Meditate. Kiss a dog. Doing stuff like this a couple of times a week helps to keep you grounded and aware of the things that really matter in life.

5. Find a Hobby.

Hobbies build skills and knowledge that will give you a sense of purpose in life. You just can't be about your workouts and job. Choose what pleases you. Your favorite hobbies will probably change over time but this is only a sign of progress. It's nice to have fun activities to look forward to!

6. Give Back to Others.

Some of the most important things you can do for your mental health is to do something nice for someone. When you feel like you've lost contact with any of the people that you care for, reach out to them and do something sweet. Doing something for someone else is only because one of the most blissful things you can do, and without the expectation of a return. The other person should not even be someone who you know. Are you stopping in the morning to get coffee when you're going to work? Pay for the person right behind you. You've done something nice to feel good about AND you have put an optimistic spin right off the bat on their day. Who knows, maybe they will be encourage to do the same. If this world needs one thing, it is more compassion.

7. Talk About Your Feelings.

Keeping your feelings locked inside is not good. You may not want to burden anyone else with your issues, but sharing them will help you work through your them. When you don't want to talk it out, consider writing in a journal. Not only would you have shared the feelings, but you can also go back and look at what you've written and understand yourself better.

8. Review Your Life Regularly.

Time stops for no one. The older we get, the easier it seems to fly. If you have a list of goals that you would like to achieve, don't forget to pause, check-in with yourself and track your progress. Sit down every few months, and look frankly at what you're doing in life. You can monitor your success and mark places that you want to develop.

9. Focus on What You Can Control.

Not everything will go as planned. And that is fine. Worrying about things you can't control would only stress you out. See what you will be in charge of. If this task always appears to be too large, split it up into smaller tasks. There'll always be something that you can't control in life. Identify it, and let go of it.

10. Use Failure to Promote Success.

If you get super bummed out after a failing, try to learn from it.

You may want to give up, but there is a lesson each time we struggle that will help us grow. Learn from these errors, and do the next time around better. When you allow yourself to wallow in failure, you will be convinced you can't. But you actually can. How do you maintain a healthy mindset?

10 WAYS TO PROMOTE A HEALTHY MINDSET

Being healthy is not about eating well and exercising, mental health also plays a major role in your overall well-being, but many of us fail to check-in and make time for a balanced mentality to practice. Around 1 in 4 Australians experience some form of mental illness, while others may experience occasional feelings of stress, lack of confidence or frustrated feelings.

There are a variety of different things you can do to cultivate a healthier attitude, from running to meditating, we share ten things you can do to encourage a healthy mindset and to support your best feeling.

1. **Eat well**

Research supports a diet of highly processed foods, with little nutrients, not only impacts the body but also the mind. Healthy nutrition from the inside out makes you feel good.

2. **Surround yourself with optimistic people**

Take the time to communicate with friends and family and the people around you. You'll feel happier and more comfortable by surrounding yourself with positive people. Many of us are running busy schedules, but it's important to make time to have fun and socialize.

3. **Take time to practice gratitude.**
   It can be easy to forget to reflect for a minute or so and to think about the things you are thankful for in your life. Something as easy as having a cup of tea without technology, or meditation can go a long way in feeling happier and encouraging peace of mind.

4. **Avoid self-comparison**
   For many people, comparison can take its toll resulting in a lower self-esteem or a lower sense of self-worth. Take comfort in the fact that nothing is the same and try to make time every now and then to disconnect from social media platforms.

5. **Find a hobby**
   A balance between study and work and time spent doing things that make you happy will make a major difference to a healthy mindset. Do something new or take a lesson to make you feel fulfilled.

6. **Giving back**
   Giving back to the community can help create meaningful connections with those around you, but it can also make your mentality stronger. Throughout the day, volunteer within your community or show small acts of kindness to those around you, and you'll feel better and happier.

7. **Talk about your feelings.**

It's important to share how we feel with people who are close to us. When you don't feel confident expressing your feelings with others, a personal journal will also help you to express what you experience.

8. **Reflect**

Making time to reflect is a powerful thing. Make time to reflect on the past day or week and talk about how you fixed problems and how it felt. Reflection is a perfect way to stick to yourself, learn and maintain a fresh mind.

9. **Exercise**

Many studies support the belief that exercise is very important in improving mental health. According to Knapen et. Al. (2014) exercise can boost body image, quality of life, resilience, and can also help in mild to moderate depression circumstances.

10. **Use failure to encourage success.**

Failure can be the foundation of personal development and growth. Only remember to pick yourself up again and try again!

CHAPTER 4
REDUCE ADDICTION-CAUSED ANXIETY AND STRESS

Stress and Anxiety

What are stress and anxiety?

Most people sometimes experience stress and anxiety. Stress is any demand that's put on your brain or body. People may report feeling stressed when they are put upon several competing demands. One event that makes you feel nervous or frustrated may activate the feeling of being stressed. Anxiety is a feeling of fear, anxiety or uneasiness. It can be a response to stress, or it can occur in individuals who cannot identify major stressors in their lives.

Stress and anxiety don't always get worse. They will help you overcome a problem or a dangerous situation in the short term. Symptoms of everyday stress and anxiety include stressing about finding a job, feeling nervous before a major exam, or being uncomfortable in certain social situations. If we haven't felt any anxiety, we might not be motivated to do things we need to do (for example, studying for that tough exam!).

Nonetheless, if stress and anxiety begin to interfere with your daily life, this can signify a more serious problem. If you avoid circumstances because of unreasonable fears, constantly worrying, or experience extreme anxiety about a traumatic incident weeks after it has occurred, it might be time to seek assistance.

What do Stress and Anxiety Feel Like?

Stress and anxiety can cause physical as well as psychological symptoms. People experience different anxiety and stress differently. Physical symptoms common to all include:

- headache

- rapid breathing

- fast heartbeat

- stomachache

- muscle tension

- sweating

- shaking

- change in appetite

- fatigue

- trouble sleeping

- diarrhea

- dizziness

- frequent urination

Anxiety and stress can also cause mental or emotional symptoms. Which may include:

- feelings of impending doom

- irrational anger

- restlessness

- panic or nervousness, especially in social settings

- difficulty concentrating

People who have long periods of stress and anxiety may experience negative health-related outcomes. These are more likely to develop high blood pressure, diabetes, heart disease,

and can also experience panic disorder and depression.

What causes anxiety and stress?

Stress and anxiety do come and go for most people. Typically, they happen after specific events in life, but then they go away.

Common causes

Common stressors include:

- having a friend or family member who is ill or injured

- death of a family member or friend

- moving

- starting a new school or job

- having an illness or injury

- getting married

- having a baby

Drugs and Medications

Drugs containing stimulants can make stress and anxiety symptoms worse. Daily use of caffeine, illicit drugs like cocaine and even alcohol can also aggravate the symptoms.

Prescription medications that can make the symptoms worse include:

- asthma inhalers

- thyroid medications

- diet pills

Stress and Anxiety-related Disorders

Stress and anxiety that occur regularly or seem out of proportion to the stressor may be indicators of an anxiety disorder. An estimated 40 million Americans live with an anxiety disorder of some kind.

People with these disorders can experience anxiety and stress on a daily basis and for prolonged periods of time. Such conditions may include:

- Generalized anxiety disorder (GAD) is a rising anxiety disorder characterized by uncontrollable worries. Often people are concerned about negative things that happen to them or to their loved ones and at other times they might not be able to find any source of concern.

- **Panic disorder is a condition that triggers panic attacks, which are moments of extreme anxiety followed by a pounding heart, fear of impending doom, and shortness of breath.**

- **Post-traumatic stress disorder (PTSD) is a condition causing hallucinations or anxiety arising from a traumatic encounter.**

- **Social phobia is a disorder that induces extreme anxiety sensations in conditions involving contact with others.**

- **Obsessive-compulsive disorder is a disease that induces repetitive thoughts and desire for certain ritual actions to be completed**

When to Seek Help

If you have thoughts of hurting yourself or others, then you can receive urgent medical assistance. Stress and anxiety are treatable disorders, and they can improve with many tools, techniques and therapies. When you can't contain your thoughts, and stress affects your daily life, speak to your primary care provider about ways to relieve stress and anxiety.

Techniques to Manage Stress and Anxiety

From time to time, it is normal to experience stress and anxiety and there are methods that you can use to make them more manageable. Pay attention to how the body and mind react to circumstances that are stressful and cause anxiety. You'll be able to predict your response the next time a traumatic event happens and it will be less disruptive.

Managing daily stress and anxiety

Certain changes in lifestyle can help relieve stress and anxiety symptoms. Both methods can be used in conjunction with traditional anxiety therapies. Stress and anxiety managing strategies include:

- getting enough sleep

- getting regular exercise

- meditating

- eating a balanced, healthy diet

- limiting caffeine and alcohol consumption

- scheduling time for hobbies

- recognizing the factors that trigger your stress

- talking to a friend

- keeping a diary of your feelings

- practicing deep breathing

Be careful if you tend to use substances such as drugs or alcohol to deal with stress and anxiety. It can lead to severe drug abuse problems that can worsen stress and anxiety.

Seek medical assistance to deal with stress and anxiety

There are several ways to seek treatment for anxiety and stress. If you feel you cannot cope with stress and anxiety, your primary care provider can recommend you see a provider of mental health care. I may use psychotherapy, also known as talk therapy, to help you work through your anxiety and stress. Your therapist can also teach you relaxation methods that will help you deal with stress.

A common and effective approach for managing anxiety is cognitive behavioral therapy (CBT). This form of therapy helps you to identify and change anxious thoughts and behaviors into more optimistic ones.

Exposure therapy and systemic desensitization can be beneficial for phobias treatment. We involve introducing you slowly to anxiety-provoking triggers to better control your feeling of fear.

Medications

The primary care provider can also prescribe medicine to help treat an anxiety condition that has been diagnosed. This may include selective serotonin reuptake inhibitors (SSRIs) such as paroxetine (Paxil) or sertraline (Zoloft). Providers often use anti-anxiety medications (benzodiazepines), such as or lorazepam (Ativan), or diazepam (Valium). Still, these methods are typically used on a short-term basis because of the risk of addiction.

What is the long-term outlook for stress and anxiety?

Stress and anxiety can be unpleasant to deal with. When untreated for long periods, they can also have detrimental effects on your physical health. While there is likely to be some amount of stress and anxiety in life and should not be cause for concern, it is important to understand when the stress in your life is having negative consequences. If you feel your stress and anxiety becomes unmanageable, look for professional assistance or ask others to help you find the support you need.

Does Stress Cause Addiction?

Historically, addiction was believed to result from consumption of an "addictive" substance, such as heroin or alcohol. Such substances were believed to have almost magical powers, making the user helpless over their use, irrespective of context and situations such as the user's stress. The DSM-IV definition of substance dependence focused on these substances' physiological effects and tolerance and withdrawal mechanisms as essential to addiction.

Since the 1970s, however, work has started to emerge that paints a different image of stress and dependency. Not only has it become clear that certain people who take "addictive" substances are not becoming addicted, but also that seemingly normal habits, not involving ingesting substances, have started to be recognized as addictive, including problem gambling, food addiction, computer addiction, shopping addiction, and even sex addiction. The set and setting and other contextual issues, such as the stress felt by the person taking the addictive substance or engaging in addictive behavior, are increasingly recognized as affecting whether or not people become addicted. The more recent findings are reflected in the DSM-V.

How Addiction is Used to Deal with Stress

Addiction often seems to be an attempt to deal with stress in a way that doesn't work quite well for the individual. While the drug or behavior you become addicted to can provide some temporary relief from stress, that relief is short-lived, so you need more to continue coping with stress. Because many addictions carry with them additional stress, such as the effects of withdrawal experienced when a drug wears off, even more of the addictive substance or activity is required to cope with the additional stress.

It is obvious from this viewpoint that some people are more vulnerable to addictions than others, simply because of the amount of tension they have in their lives. For example, there is now a well-established correlation between childhood violence, whether physical, emotional or sexual abuse and the subsequent development of substance and behavioral addictions. Childhood abuse is particularly traumatic to the child, but it tends to trigger issues as the child matures as an adult, with subsequent relationship and self-esteem issues. Not everyone who has been abused as a child develops an addiction and not everyone with addiction in childhood has been abused.

The vulnerability of child abuse survivors to subsequent addiction is a direct indication of the correlation between stress and addiction.

Although stress doesn't cause addiction on its own — many people are under stress and do not become an alcoholic — it plays a major role for others. Recognition of the role of stress in the development of addiction and the importance of stress management in preventing and overcoming addiction is important in helping people to avoid the pain that addiction can bring to both addicts and their loved ones. It is never too early to teach young people and children good stress management skills, so they are less inclined to become addicted.

HOW DEPRESSION, ANXIETY AND ADDICTION GO TOGETHER AND WHY IT MATTERS

T he most surprising statistic I have read about mental health is as follows: more than 50 percent of people in America will experience a mental disorder at some stage in their lives. This data comes from a report conducted by Harvard Medical School and the National Mental Health Institute (NIMH).

Take a moment to allow this to sink in. Then ask yourself, how much do we know about those circumstances that affect most of us in our lives at some point? Mental health issues aren't "side problems" they affect millions of Americans every day.

This year's National Depression Screening Day is on October 8, and the World Mental Health Day follows on October 10. Now is the perfect time to focus on depression and anxiety, two interrelated conditions of mental and emotional health which often precipitate addiction.

Depression and Anxiety by the Numbers

More than 8.3 million American adults have depression and anxiety, according to a 2017 report released in the journal Psychiatric Services. Plus, the 2016 Surgeon General's addiction report notes that in 2015, more than 27 million people abused drugs and more than 66 million abused alcohol.

Depression, anxiety, and addiction are growing, and they are all intertwined. However, let's describe those words before we think about why depression and anxiety contribute to drug addiction.

Defining Anxiety and Depression

Depression and anxiety are traditional textbook definitions which describe symptoms, not causes.

If you google "depression," you'll get this: "A mental health disorder characterized by persistently depressed mood." If you search for "anxiety," you'll find this: "A mental health disorder characterized by feelings of worry, anxiety, or fear." These definitions are accurate, but they're not exactly illuminating. The root causes aren't revealed.

We like to define depression as "anger turned inward." It's only three words in length, but it gets right to the heart of the matter. Depression is anger you weren't allowed to feel or express yourself. Though depression manifests in the form of numb apathy or sadness, it begins as anger.

Similarly, we define anxiety as "emotional energy bouncing back and forth, caught between the inner walls." Anxiety is the feeling you get when you refuse to feel your "off-limits," such as anger and hurt.

We teach a structure that clarifies the relationship between anxiety, depression, and addiction. It's called the "Anger-Hurt-Loving" model, and it points the path to recovery.

Depression, Anxiety, and Addiction

The Anger-Hurt-Loving model peels the curtain back and allows us to glimpse what usually drives addictive behaviors: untreated mental and emotional health problems. The model is also crucial to understanding anger and addiction.

Here's what it looks like

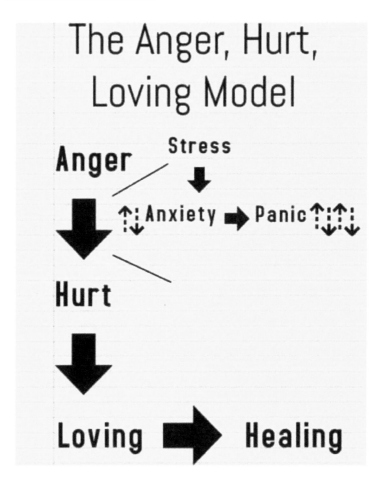

Here is an explanation of how it functions:

- There is an underlying hurt behind any feeling of wrath. When there's something we can't handle or what we need is absent, we get angry. Anyway, the reason we're angry is that it hurts a part of us.

- However, many of us were socialized not to feel our anger or express it, so we force it down and inward. The model's first diagonal line reflects how we cut off from the feeling of anger. Anger turned inward becomes depression.

- We've refused to feel our anger now, chances are we don't even want to feel our hurts. (Who would like to feel hurt? It hurts!) And we also cut off from that painful feeling experience, thus the second diagonal line on the model.

- Because we don't feel our hurt or anger, our emotional energy, that is, the up-and-down arrows in the model, bounces back and forth between our inner walls.

So, what do we call the bouncing back and forth of emotional energy? That's right; this is anxiety.

Likewise, we define panic as "anxiety acceleration." If anxiety is an emotional jog, then panic is a sprint.

How Addiction Plays In

And now we're anxious, depressed, and at the point of panic. We feel miserable and desperate to feel good. And sometimes the bar isn't even that high; we just feel so bad for a break! We want our feelings of anxiety, stress, and panic to be avoided, so we resort to substances. We use it not because we are bad, but because we feel bad.

Fortunately, there is a different option. Like you see in the picture, you step toward healing when you encourage yourself to feel your feelings rather than covering them up.

The best way to sum up the key message of the Anger-Hurt-Loving Model is this: When you apply love to the hurting parts of yourself, you recover.

You might think, Wait a minute, what about my medications? Don't they help me recover too?

The Role of Medications in Healing

While self-medication with illegal substances is dangerous, taking legally prescribed medications such as SSRIs for depression and anxiety can do a lot of good. Prescription drugs can help and stabilize people with mood disorders ... to some extent.

(Important clarification: we are not talking here about antipsychotic medications, since they are a separate class of medications with different protocols.)

Depression medicine can well be the right solution in the short term. But, in the long term, addressing the root causes is critical, not just alleviating the symptoms.

I do want to make people feel better. I want to provide crisis care. However, I want to provide people with the support they need to heal from depression and anxiety too.

Usually, I recommend people to maintain their current medications and dosages while they continue to resolve the underlying core issues. When they've been given enough time to meet with a doctor, they can determine if a lower dosage is needed. I

also see chronic mental health issues decreasing in severity-or even totally disappearing! – As people begin to show love to the part of themselves that hurt.

How to Treat Depression and Anxiety for Recovery

What is really behind your anxiety, mood swings, your depression? It's time to find out. It's time to treat the mental health problems instead of just medicating them and hope they're going to go away.

As you now know, lasting recovery from substance abuse involves treating and repairing the underlying core issues that originally triggered depression and anxiety. So, give yourself the tools and encouragement to deal through the anger and hurt you've been keeping in place. This could well mean ambulatory treatment. Perhaps this means seeking inpatient depression treatment. Everyone is different, but nobody should have to do it alone.

If you're afraid to feel and afraid to try, don't be. In offering this love and care to yourself, you will find that you are far stronger than you know.

As speaker and author Anne Lamott wrote:

"Hope begins in the dark, the persistent belief that the dawn will come if you just show up and try to do the right thing. You wait, watch, and work: you do not give up."

CHAPTER 5

ANXIETY DISORDERS AND DRUG ADDICTION

A pproximately 18% of the U.S. population suffers from some form of anxiety disorder. Those who do are about two to three times more likely to have addiction problems than those who do not have anxiety. When a person has both substance disorder and mental health, this is known as dual diagnosis. Treatment can tackle both conditions.

Substance Abuse and Anxiety

Everyone experiences anxiety and stress. While most people may experience anxiety often in a fleeting way, the anxiety may be unrelated to some specific situation for a person with an anxiety disorder. And, it could be completely out of proportion to the actual situation. A severe anxiety problem affects your ability to function in your everyday life.

Some individuals with anxiety have a dual diagnosis, meaning they both have a mental condition, such as anxiety, and a substance abuse disorder. For these cases, it can be difficult to say which came first: the anxiety disorder or the substance abuse disorder. Some people with anxiety may use alcohol or drugs to self-medicate or better manage their symptoms.

Comorbidity is common with substance abuse and anxiety; this means people frequently face the 2 conditions together. Approximately 20 percent of those with anxiety or mood disorder have substance abuse problems, just as approximately 20 percent of those with a substance abuse problem have anxiety or mood disorder.

Risk Factors

While anxiety and the substance abuse are separate disorders, they carry common risk factors like:

- Genetic vulnerability. Genetic components can have some similarity that increases a person's susceptibility to developing both anxiety and addiction and disorders.

- Environmental triggers. Examples include abuse and trauma, which can also lead to anxiety as well as increased vulnerability to substance use.

- Involvement of similar brain regions. The functioning of the brain is also a common factor in both forms of disorder. For people with anxiety and other mental health conditions, main brain regions that respond to reward and stress and are affected by drugs may also show irregularities.

- Developmental stages. It is likely that teenage drug use can affect certain brain functions in a way that makes them more vulnerable to drug effects and contributes to anxiety disorders.

Symptoms

There are several types of anxiety disorders, with symptoms varying slightly. The generalized anxiety disorder (GAD) symptoms include:

- An inability to concentrate.

- Being irritable.

- Tense muscles.

- Being unable to control worrying.

- Feeling restless or on edge.

- Getting tired easily.

- Problems getting to sleep, feeling rested, or staying asleep.

Panic disorder includes symptoms such as:

- Worries and fears of another attack occurring.

- Sudden attacks of fear.

- Avoiding places in which attacks have occurred.

- Loss of control over the feelings of fear.

People with social anxiety have symptoms such as:

- Getting sick physically when having to interact with others.

- Difficulty interacting with others.

- Avoiding people as much as possible.

- Blushing, sweating, or having issues speaking when others are around.

- Being very worried about judgment by others.

- Having difficulty making and keeping friends.

A variety of symptoms are associated with addiction to alcohol and drugs. An individual may be diagnosed with a substance abuse disorder if they display at least 2 of these symptoms at any point in the past twelve months:

- Taking more of the drug than they expected.

- Continued usage despite being mindful of the legal ramifications.

- Continued use, despite knowledge of the adverse effects of the medication (for instance, emotional health or deteriorating medical).

- Strong craving for the substance of abuse.

- Inability to cut back on using drugs or alcohol.

- Failure to do what you are supposed to do at school, at home, or at work, and failure to fulfil your obligations due to alcohol or drugs.

- Alcohol or drugs take on greater significance than previous interests or hobbies.

- Doing irresponsible things, like driving while on drugs or alcohol.

- Alcohol and drugs typically eat up your time. Whether you're using drugs and alcohol, or you're trying to get over it, or you're trying to get more alcohol and drugs.

- Increased tolerance of the alcoholic or drug substance to where more is required to develop the desired feelings. Stopping use or cutting back triggers withdrawal symptoms.

ANXIETY AFTER DRUG USE

Sometimes during or after drug use, a person can experience panic attacks or general anxiety. The Mental Disorders Diagnostic and Statistical Manual explain that if the anxiety occurs during or soon after intoxication and leads to impairment in social or occupational functioning, a person may be diagnosed with a substance-induced anxiety disorder.

Drugs that may cause anxiety disorder with the substance include alcohol, PCP (phencyclidine), inhalants, stimulants, and hallucinogens.

Other drugs can cause anxiety when the person starts taking the medications and withdrawal experiences. Usually, this form of anxiety occurs with drugs that inhibit the central nervous system and relieve anxiety, including benzodiazepines, opioids, and

alcohol.

Symptoms of drug-induced anxiety from withdrawal can include:

- Shaking.

- Elevated blood pressure.

- Hyperactivity.

- Agitation.

For some people, marijuana reduces anxiety. Others may actually experience increased anxiety, though, particularly when they use marijuana at higher doses. Many individuals, genetic, and environmental factors can lead to marijuana-induced anxiety. Women, those who rarely use marijuana and those with pre-existing anxiety disorders are more vulnerable to marijuana-induced anxiety than others.

Treatment

When a person has both a mental illness such as anxiety and a substance use disorder, all conditions must be treated. A person who only completes drug recovery and does not receive anxiety treatment is more likely to experience medical complications, suicide or early death.

In addition to living a healthy lifestyle, which requires exercise, a healthy diet, and proper nutrition, both conditions may be treated with medication. But if treatment combines the drugs with therapy, the person would likely have a better outcome.

Medications

Anxiety disorders are also treated with antidepressants medication. Commonly used antidepressants include both SNRIs (selective norepinephrine inhibitors) and SSRIs (selective serotonin reuptake inhibitors). Some people may be prescribed benzodiazepines for short-term anxiety control which include drugs such as Valium and Xanax.

The risk of addiction, however, makes such drugs less than ideal for people with history of drug abuse.

Alcoholism can be treated with disulfiram (Antabuse) and acamprosate (Campral). These drugs produce an unpleasant reaction when one drinks and, respectively, decreases withdrawal symptoms. Naltrexone, a drug used to treat opioid addiction, can also work in the treatment of alcohol addiction.

For people with opioid dependence, there are many medication-assisted drugs for recovery. As in treatment for alcohol dependence, naltrexone can be used to block some of the opioid's rewarding effects, thus discouraging continued use.

Other medicines, such as buprenorphine and methadone, tend to stop the cravings and relapse of opioid-related symptoms, making them helpful during detox and maintenance therapy.

Therapies

Numerous therapies help treat addiction and anxiety. The most popular addiction treatments are:

- Cognitive behavioral therapy, or CBT, helps change a person's mindset about drugs and using strategies to cope with the stress. CBT also helps a person learn how to identify drug addiction triggers and how to prevent or cope with these triggers.

- Motivational interviewing. This approach increases the

ability of an individual to get involved in the process of change. Among those who need addiction treatment, ambivalence can be found, particularly if a court or legal program has ordered the treatment program. Instead of ignoring this ambivalence, motivational interviewing identifies that and tries to help people work through it.

- Contingency management. This uses rewards, such as vouchers or gift cards for negative drug screens to help people stay engaged in treatment.

- Matrix Model.

- This method is most widely used to treat stimulants addiction to. The program utilizes urine drug screens, 12-step groups, individual therapy, family therapy, and drug education.

- Exposure therapy. This form of CBT therapy slowly introduces the person to a situation or an object that makes them very anxious. At each stage of the process, they are taught to manage the anxiety.

- Relaxation training. Relaxation training is often a part of exposure therapy and CBT. Mindfulness is also integrated and can include meditation or the visualization of relaxing scenes. Furthermore, the training involves self-soothing methods, such as using oils and scents. Physical relaxation involves learning to relax muscles, doing activities such as yoga, and breathing calmly.

- Breathing training. Breathing training involves learning to breathe deeply, from the diaphragm, holding the breath, and exhaling gradually, all of which will usually help a person feel less anxious.

Anxiety disorders are most often treated with CBT. For disorders such as panic disorders or social anxiety, the number of patients receive 12 to 16 sessions over a span of 3 to 4 months. The anxiety disorders, however, appear to be chronic. Recurrence is common even after treatment. Some people require a longer recovery plan which can last up to 50 sessions or more than a year.

Recovery Programs

Recovery programs are widely available. Forms of treatment include:

- Inpatient treatment. An inpatient program will offer 24/7 medical, supervision, and social support to help a person stop using drugs while also learning how to manage their anxiety.

- Outpatient treatment. For some people, outpatient treatment programs can be an option to receive anxiety and addiction treatment. Outpatient treatment programs vary in how often a person is attending treatment. Most outpatient programs may meet at a time for only one day or 2 per week, for 2 to 3 hours. Some programs, however, include an intensive outpatient program, or IOP, which normally meets for 2-3 days a week, generally 3-4 hours a day. Other treatment programs provide what is known as partial hospitalization, or PHP, which typically meets 4-6 hours a day, from five to seven days a week.

Often, such programs are the initial stage of treatment. Other times, people will attend PHP or IOP as a step away from a more serious type of treatment, such as hospital treatment. Service intensity is contingent upon individual needs.

Other types of programs that may be incorporated into outpatient or inpatient programs or used as follow-up care to treatment include:

- Twelve-step programs. Such programs are usually an aftercare form for someone who has been through a course of outpatient and/or inpatient treatment. However,

- some people are using them as their main source of recovery. These groups are vital to ongoing sobriety and support.

- Support groups. This can be run by a therapist or other individuals who have been dealing with or have dealt with anxiety. These groups are useful in finding other people in the same situation as you, and in learning how to handle their own anxiety.

HOW TO STOP SMOKING AND STAY CALM IN THE

PROCESS

The coronavirus (COVID-19) pandemic has changed the way we all live our lives. A new world of practices of self-isolation and social distancing will likely remain in place for some time to slow the spread of the virus.

This may leave you feeling more worried, anxious, and stressed because you lack the social interaction that makes you feel connected and optimistic.

You may feel overwhelmed by additional concerns about your health, the health of your family and your job. Such feelings can affect anyone and are difficult to deal with, and can make it particularly difficult to stop smoking at this time.

Good Thinking and Stop Smoking London have teamed up with that in mind to give smokers some tips on how to quit – and how to remain calm in the process.

Understand the Role Anxiety Plays in Smoking

We know it can be difficult to quit smoking, and it can feel especially difficult at this time. Some of you may turn to cigarettes in the belief that smoking is going to help to relieve stress and anxiety – but it does not! Smoking relieves symptoms of nicotine withdrawal such as irritability and low mood-tricking you into thinking that it helps with stress. It has been shown that people who stop smoking have less depression, anxiety, and stress, plus improved mood compared to those who keep smoking.

1. **Use deep breathing and meditation to help reduce stress and anxiety.**

Using proven guided meditation and visualization methods is a great way to feel calmer when you stop smoking. Not only does this make you better, but it will also help you make certain healthier lifestyle choices.

2. **Make a quit plan**

You can move forward confidently with your stop-smoking journey by giving yourself time to prepare. Get support and use a stop smoking medication, such as a patch and another nicotine product, or some prescription medications, to greatly increase your chances of stopping successfully.

It also helps prepare yourself for those situations and feelings that may cause you to smoke.

3. **Get lots of sleep**

Sleep disturbances are a common side effects of nicotine withdrawal. Lack of sleep will make it feel so much harder like quitting smoking. So, getting on top of any sleep problems that you may encounter quickly is especially important.

4. **Exercise daily**

Scheduling outdoor exercise as often as you wish is recommended and is good for you – as long as you meet the recommendations for social distance.

Exercising 30 minutes a day is a perfect self-help practice to get the endorphins flowing and improve strength. When you stop smoking, you can find that you have less coughing and shortness of breath as your lungs recover, which makes exercise easier. It will also improve your mood by being more involved, relieving stress and help you to sleep better.

5. Don't do it by yourself, ask for help

The final tip is to see how you feel about these feelings and be compassionate. It may help you to speak about them with your family and friends using phone or video calls. Online communities are also there to help you stop smoking.

CHAPTER 6
WAYS TO RELIEVE INSOMNIA WHEN YOU QUIT SMOKING

New ex-smokers during the process of smoking cessation will sleep more than normal. This can leave you feeling confused and lethargic as your body responds to the loss of multiple doses of nicotine and other chemicals during the day.

If this describes how you feel, do not fight off the need for extra sleep.

Take naps when you can, and get to bed earlier than usual. With a little rest, the body's going to bounce back. On the opposite side of the spectrum are the ex-smokers who have trouble getting to sleep at all. Insomnia is a common symptom of withdrawal from nicotine.

If you experience insomnia in the first few weeks after you stopped smoking, try some of these natural remedies to relieve your uneasiness.

1. Cut Your Caffeine Intake in Half

Smokers metabolize caffeine much more easily than non-smokers do. Smokers must also drink more caffeine to achieve the same effects as non-smokers.

If you stop smoking without lowering the consumption of caffeine, the body gradually becomes over-caffeinated, which can make you feel irritable and jittery. You may not be able to drink as much as you did as a smoker, though you don't need to cut caffeine out completely.

Start by reducing your consumption of caffeine by at least 50 percent This should give you the right amount of caffeine without feeling the symptoms of caffeine withdrawal or being over-caffeinated.

Gradually lower your intake of caffeine instead of going "cold turkey". Quitting caffeine altogether can lead to uncomfortable symptoms of withdrawal.

2. Take a Warm Bath

Light a few scented candles, use some fragrant bath salts and let go of the day's stress. A warm bath is a perfect way to relax and prepare the body and mind for sleep.

3. Schedule a Massage

Enlist your partner or other willing pair of hands to help work your muscles relieve the stress. Although a luxurious full body massage is fantastic, even 10 or 15 minutes spent on your shoulders, face, neck, and scalp can work wonders to help you unwind and get ready for a good night's sleep.

4. Drink a Cup of Tea

There are a variety of herbal teas specifically blended to help soothe and promote sleep. Take a look at the supermarket's tea section or visit your local health food store and ask for suggestions.

5. Listen to Soothing Music

Soothing, mellow music will help you to relax enough to drift off to sleep. Try to listen to a sound of waves lapping on the beach. Sounds of rain, thunder, and sounds of nature can be relaxing too. If you're listening to music on your phone or tablet while you fall asleep, make sure that it is set to automatically turn off.

You don't want to get up and do it yourself, because that's defeating the object.

6. Create a Digital Curfew

Using electronic equipment before bedtime will make it more difficult for you to fall and stay asleep. That is because the artificial blue light produced by devices such as smartphones, tablets and laptops suppresses melatonin production, the sleep-regulating hormone.

Consider turning off your electronics one to two hours prior to going to bed. Try to incorporate wind-down practices such as reading (an actual written book, not one on your phone) or meditation instead of screen time, to get your body ready for a good night's rest.

7. Drink a Glass of Warm Milk

Warm milk improves your sleep because it is full of a sleep-inducing amino acid known as tryptophan. The neurotransmitter serotonin, which is then transformed into the hormone melatonin, is produced by the body using tryptophan.

Your brain has more tryptophan available when you consume a carbohydrate along with it. No wonder milk and cookies have long been a popular snack in bedtime.

Other foods that contain tryptophan include:

- Fish

- Cheese

- Eggs

- Seeds (including sunflower seeds)

- Nuts (such as cashews, almonds, pistachios, and hazelnuts)

- Soy products (such as tofu and soy sauce)

- Poultry (such as turkey and chicken)

L-tryptophan supplements are usually not recommended, because they were historically associated with syndrome of eosinophilia-myalgia. Food and drink containing L-tryptophan, of course, are better options.

8. Don't Drink Alcohol.

Although a drink or two may initially make it easier to fall asleep, alcohol avoidance is best. Alcohol suppresses rapid eye movement (REM) sleep, ensuring you won't feel relaxed in the morning, even if you sleep through the evening. Alcohol in your body can also interrupt your sleep and cause you to wake up repeatedly during the night

9. Get Some Exercise

If you can't sleep, try to get out a few hours before bed for a good long stroll. Just a 15-minute walk will help. However, timing is vital with this one. Try to stop intense exercise at least one hour before bedtime because it can make it harder to fall asleep.

10. Relaxation Methods

Try meditation and progressive muscle relaxation at the end of a busy day, to ease your mind and relax your muscles.

Lie down with your eyes closed, try these simple relaxation methods in bed. Start to tense and relax the muscles throughout your body as an alternative, starting with your feet and working your way up.

Then, move on to your mental thoughts. Recognize each when it comes to mind and then let it go. Let the mind float and drift, relieving worry and stress as it goes.

11. Don't Nap During the Day.

While finally getting some shut-eye may feel good, if it's during the day, don't do it. If you are struggling with insomnia, power naps aren't your friend. You'll pay for it when it is time for bed.

12. Start Your Day a little earlier.

Another effective strategy is to start your day a little earlier to help you change your internal clock. You can also use the extra time to meditate – a win, a win.

The physical withdrawal phase of smoking cessation is a temporary condition. Your sleep habits would quickly return to normal if you had no insomnia before you stopped smoking. If symptoms continue for the first month or so, arrange an appointment with your doctor to ensure that smoking cessation is responsible for how you feel.

CHAPTER 7
POSITIVE AFFIRMATIONS TO QUIT
SMOKING

F ed up with smoking?

Are you ready to heal your nicotine addiction?

Here is a list of the best positive affirmations and quotes that will help you stop smoking so you can control your life more.

Best Affirmations If You Want to Stop Smoking

1. I have decided to stop smoking, and it feels good.

2. I love myself more. I say "no" to smoking and "yes" to life.

3. It's easy to quit smoking.

4. I gain nothing as a smoker.

5. As a non-smoker I have a lot to gain.

6. Choosing to be free of nicotine is a choice which I am glad to make.

7. I just breathe and let go, anytime I need a break.

8. I care about my body and let go of addictions which are unhealthy.

9. I hereby release any need to smoke with open arms and accept a smoke-free life.

10. Smoking is no real fun, that's why I would find it easy to quit.

11. This is the moment I choose freedom from smoking.

12. I prefer a daily breath of fresh air.

13. Because I know myself better every day, I know how to easily quit smoking.

14. Quitting smoking takes no power because I do not want to smoke.

15. I'm going to be free from smoking and do it happily.

16. I'll stop smoking easily.

17. My natural state is that of a non-smoker.

18. Knowing I have control over my life decisions, including smoking, is empowering.

19. I opt for good health.

20. I look to the future with excitement, as a non-smoker.

21. My life as a non-smoker would be healthier.

22. I look forward to living a cigarette-free life.

Best Stop Smoking If You've Already Quit

1. Each day I feel happy and better in every way.

2. I prefer a daily breath of fresh air.

3. Every day, my lungs feel better.

4. I live a smoke-free life now, and that feels fantastic.

5. I choose not to smoke, and that feels good.

6. I appreciate that new sense of freedom I have as a non-smoker.

7. As a non-smoker today, I am engaged in activities that support my well-being.

8. My body is nicotine-free, and feels good.

9. Now I can say "I don't smoke". That gives me an immense sense of pride.

10. I love my body deeply and respect it.

11. As a non-smoker, my self-image increases every day.

12. I move away from smoking, towards a new, healthier me every single day.

13. Each day, my breathing is improving.

14. Being smoke-free, I now feel complete ease in all situations.

15. It's easy to eliminate Nicotine from my life.

16. Today, I'm free to smoke, and I'm really happy about it.

17. My lungs are becoming healthy and clean.

18. As a non-smoker, I am calm and relaxed.

19. Being free from cigarettes feels amazing.

20. As a non-smoker, my life gets better every day in every way.

21. I am so grateful that I have opted to give up cigarettes for health and happiness.

22. I feel happy when I wake up with the choice I made to be smoke-free.

Affirmations to Stop Smoking Forever

1. I never want to smoke again.

2. I let go of the urge to smoke.

3. Smoking no longer serves me.

4. I have control over my life.

5. I'm delighted to be breathing fresh air.

6. My lungs are clean and healthy.

7. I let go of my smoking addiction.

8. I can quickly conquer my smoking addiction.

9. I'm ready to stop smoking.

Affirmations to Overcome Smoking Addiction

1. I am not an addict.

2. I take life into my hands.

3. I'm stronger than cigarettes.

4. I am not nicotine addict.

5. I am motivated to stop smoking.

6. My goal is to be healthy.

7. I don't enjoy smoking.

8. My lungs are nicotine-free.

Affirmations to Find Inner Peace

1. I'm peaceful, calm and focused.

2. I'm free from addiction.

3. I find peace through meditation or taking a walk.

4. I'm more comfortable in non-smoking environments.

5. I find happiness within myself.

6. I am feeling at peace with myself.

7. I'm feeling happy and at ease.

8. My breathing is slow and calm.

Affirmations to Release Stress and Anxiety

1. I am letting go of my worries.

2. I have absolutely nothing to worry about.

3. My anxiety is fading away gradually.

4. I release any stress-related thoughts I have.

5. I choose to focus on the good stuff.

6. I am a less anxious person every day.

7. I'm filled with peace and calm.

8. My stress is disappearing.

Affirmations to Create Healthy Habits

1. I am in control of my habits.

2. I make good choices.

3. I enjoy maintaining a healthy lifestyle.

4. I am creating the life of my dreams. One choice at a time.

5. I love nourishing my body.

6. I am happy when I exercise.

7. I enjoy eating healthy foods.

8. I am motivated to be a healthy and fit person.

9. I am grateful for my willpower.

10. I am proud of myself for my choices.

Quotes & Sayings to Help You Quit Smoking

- Take control of your life. Take control of your habits – Anonymous.

- Out of our weakness, our strength rises — Ralph Emerson Waldo.

- We become what we repeatedly do — Sean Covey.

- Consistency creates habit, and habits shape our lives.

- Cigarette smoking is like paying to shorten your life.

- Every time you light up a cigarette, you are saying your life is not worth living.

- It is at your moments of decision that your destiny is shaped – Tony Robbins.

- Smoking is harmful to the brain, hateful to your nose, and dangerous to the lungs – King James.

- Your craving is TEMPORARY, but it will damage your lungs PERMANENTLY.

- The key to breaking any bad habit successfully is to love something greater than habit – MacGill Bryant.

- We form habits first, then they form us. Conquer your bad habits, or they will conquer you eventually – Anonymous.

- To quit smoking, you must first want to quit, but then you must also do the quitting –Goethe.

- If it seems impossible to stop smoking right now, it is exactly what you should start doing – Eleanor Roosevelt.

- You really get closer to staying smoke-free each time you decide to stop smoking – Henry Ford.

- You're never going to change your life until you change something that you do every day. Your everyday routine is the secret to your success – John C. Maxwell.

Six Ways to Give Your Mind A Break:

1. Stop worrying.

2. Forget the problems weighing you down.

3. Stop stressing.

4. Lighten up.

5. Forgive others.

6. Forgive yourself — Germany Kent.

CHAPTER 8
RELAX AND FALL ASLEEP EASILY
EVERY NIGHT

It can be frustrating to not be able to fall asleep and feel the consequences the next day. People will learn to fall asleep more easily using easy, natural tips and tricks.

When someone is having trouble falling asleep, one solution is to take sleep-inducing medications. These medications, however, aren't an ideal long-term remedy.

Certain natural methods — such as providing a regular bedtime routine, avoiding screens before bedtime, doing gentle daytime exercise, reading before bedtime, and practicing other strategies of mindfulness — can help.

Different things work for different people, so take some time to find out what works for you.

This chapter looks at twenty-one natural methods that people can use to fall asleep quickly.

Twenty-one Ways to Fall Asleep Naturally

Having a consistent sleep pattern can help a person fall asleep faster.

Most people struggling with sleep lie in bed, worrying about how to fall asleep. Consider following the guidelines below when this happens. Many of them are adjustments in lifestyle for the long term, and some are short-term approaches to try straight away.

1. Create a consistent sleeping pattern

Going to bed every night at various times is a common occurrence for many. Such irregular sleeping patterns, however, may interfere with sleep because they disrupt the circadian rhythm of the body.

The circadian rhythm is a combination of behavioral, mental, and physical changes over a cycle of 24 hours. A primary role of circadian rhythm is to determine whether or not the body is ready to sleep.

A biological clock which releases hormones to induce sleep or wakefulness heavily influences this. Going to bed at the same time every night helps the body clock determine when to trigger sleep.

2. Keep the lights off.

Cues like light also affect the circadian rhythm, which helps tell the brain and body when it's night. Keeping the room as dark as possible before going to bed can help bring on to sleep.

3. Avoid napping during the day.

Taking naps during the daytime can also disrupt the circadian rhythm, particularly those which last longer than 2 hours.

One study discovered that college students who slept at least three times a week and those who slept for more than two hours each time had a lower quality of sleep than their peers who did not.

It is tempting to take a long nap after a poor night's sleep. Try to prevent this because it can adversely affect a healthy sleep cycle.

4. Get some exercise during the day.

Physical exercise affects the quality of the sleep positively.

One study that looked at 305 people above the age of 40 with sleeping problems found that exercise programs of moderate to high intensity contributed to changes in sleep quality. The study also found participants took their sleep medication less often when taking part in an exercise program.

It is still uncertain whether or not exercise is having an effect on sleep at various times of the day.

When you embark on an exercise routine, it can be hard to know where to start.

5. Avoid using your cell phone.

There is currently much debate as to whether the use of cell phones at bedtime affects sleep or not.

One research on college students found that there was a poorer sleep quality for those who scored high on a scale of problem phone use, such as addictive texting behavior.

Most of the latest research is in students and young people, and it is unknown whether these results apply to other age groups or not. Research also appears to concentrate on the issue of phone usage. People who do not use their phone in this manner may not be as prone to sleep disturbances.

In this area, more work is required to understand the extent to which phone usage can affect sleep.

6. Read a book

Reading books can be calming and can help avoid habits of worrying thoughts that could interfere with a person's sleep. It is best to avoid books which may trigger strong emotional

responses.

7. Avoid caffeine

Caffeine acts as a stimulant. This increases wakefulness and can interfere with sleep patterns. It is also best to avoid caffeine for at least four hours before bedtime.

Caffeine intake at any time of the day may have a detrimental impact on the quality of the sleep in certain people. It may be better for some individuals to avoid caffeine altogether.

8. Try meditation or mindfulness

Mindfulness and meditation can help reduce anxiety, which also disrupts sleep. Using these techniques can help to calm an anxious mind, distract the person from busy thoughts and make it easier for them to fall asleep.

A research in older adults with sleeping problems discovered that meditation increased the quality of sleep compared to people who didn't practice meditation.

9. Try counting

A longstanding method of sleep induction is to gradually count down from 100. There are a lot of theories about why this may work, including boredom and distracting the individual from anxious thoughts.

10. Change your eating habits.

What an individual eats can have an impact on their sleep, particularly in the evening. Eating a large meal within one hour of going to bed, for example, can hinder a person's ability to sleep.

It can take at least two to three hours to digest a meal. Lying down during this time can cause feelings of nausea or discomfort in certain people and slow down the digestive process.

Best to allow enough time for the body to digest a meal before lying down. The exact time it takes can vary from one person to another.

11. Get the room temperature right

Being too cold or too hot will affect a person's ability to sleep.

The temperature at which people feel most relaxed varies, so experimenting with different temperatures is necessary.

The National Sleep Foundation suggests a 60–67 ° F (16–19oC) bedroom temperature to encourage sleep.

12. Try aromatherapy

Aromatherapy has long been used by individuals to promote relaxation and sleep.

Lavender oil is a popular choice to aid sleep. A research in 31 young adults discovered that the use of lavender oil before bed had a beneficial impact on the quality of the night's sleep. After waking up, the participants reported having more energy.

13. Find a comfortable position.

Sleeping in a comfortable position is necessary. Changing positions frequently can be disruptive, but finding the right position will make a major difference to the onset of sleep.

Most people find that the best position for a good night's sleep is to lie on their side.

14. Listen to music

Though this does not work for everybody, some people benefit from listening to music that relaxes them before going to bed.

The response of a person to the music will depend on their personal preferences. Music can be distracting at times, but can cause anxiety and sleeplessness.

15. Try breathing exercises

Breathing exercises are a relaxation technique which is very popular. Practicing deep breathing or doing different breathing exercises will help de-stress people and take away worrying thoughts from their mind. It can be a tool to get to sleep.

One common option is 4-7-8 breathing. This involves breathing in for four seconds, holding the breath for 7 seconds, and exhaling for eight seconds. This kind of deep, rhythmic breathing is relaxing and may encourage sleep.

16. Take a hot bath or shower

It can be soothing to take a bath or shower and help prepare the body for sleep. This can also help enhance the control of temperature before bedtime.

Cold and hot showers have different benefits. Hot showers will help make you sleep better.

17. Avoid reading e-books

Over the past few years, e-books have become more popular.

They have backlit screens which make them perfect for reading in a dark room before bed. This may have a detrimental effect on sleep, though.

One study provided a printed book and an e-book for young adults to read before bed. The researchers found the participants had taken longer to fall asleep when using the e-book.

We were also more alert in the evenings and less alert throughout the morning due to reading the printed text. These findings suggest that e-books may have a detrimental effect on sleep.

The study did involve only 12 participants. The researchers also used a study design which meant participants were reading both kinds of books. It is difficult to determine whether or not exposure to both reading conditions has biased the results.

There are few reliable studies in this area, and any firm

conclusions need require further research.

1. Take melatonin

Melatonin is known as the sleep hormone, which is generated by the body in order to cause drowsiness and sleep in line with the body clock. People may also take it as a replacement to improve the ability to get to sleep.

2. Use a comfortable bed.

The National Sleep Foundation advises that people sleep on a comfortable mattress, and cozy, supportive pillows to get a good night's sleep. Investing in comfortable mattress may have a beneficial effect on the quality of the sleep.

3. Avoid noisy environments, if possible.

Noise can be distracting, preventing the onset of sleep and decreasing sleep quality.

A 2016 study found participants in a hospital setting had significantly worse sleep than at home. The study authors found this was mainly due to the increased noise level in the hospital.

4. Avoid excessive alcohol consumption.

Drinking copious amounts of alcohol before bed will adversely affect sleep. Alcohol is problematic because it can give rise to feelings of restlessness and nausea, which can disrupt the onset of sleep.

CHAPTER 9
DEEP SLEEP ALL NIGHT LONG

What is Deep Sleep and Why is it Important?

What to know about deep sleep?

You may have learned that between 7 and 9 hours of sleep is required for adults every night.

When you rest, the body moves through various stages of the sleep cycle. For example, deep sleep is the stage of sleep you need when you wake up in the morning to feel refreshed. Unlike rapid eye movement (REM), deep sleep is when the body and brain waves are slowing down.

It's hard to wake up from deep sleep, and you may still feel tired if you do.

What Are the Stages of Sleep?

Sleep is divided into two groups: REM and non-REM sleep. You start the night in non-REM sleep, followed by a short period of REM sleep. The cycle continues at about every 90 minutes during the night.

Deep sleep occurs in the final stage of non-REM sleep.

Non-REM sleep

Stage 1 of non-REM sleep lasts several minutes as you transition from being awake to sleeping.

During stage 1:

- Your body functions — like respiration, eye movements, and heartbeat — begin to slow down

- Your muscles relax with occasional twitches

- Your brain waves start slowing down from wakeful state

Stage two accounts for approximately 50% of the overall cycle of sleep. This is the stage of sleep you may fall into more than any other throughout the night.

During stage 2:

- Decline in core temperature

- Your body systems continue to relax and slow down

- Your eye movement stops

- Your brain waves are weak, but you do have a few short activity bursts

Stages 3 and 4 are when you experience deep sleep

During these stages:

- It's hard to awaken even with loud noises

- As your muscles relax, your heartbeat and breathing become their slowest

- Your brain waves become the slowest they will be while you are asleep

Deep sleep is also known as "slow-wave sleep" (SWS) or delta sleep.

The first deep sleep stage lasts from 45 to 90 minutes. During the first half of the night, it lasts for longer periods and gets shorter with each sleep cycle.

REM sleep

Stage 5, or the first stage of REM sleep, occurs after going through non-REM periods for around 90 minutes.

During this stage:

- Your eyes move rapidly from side to side

- You experience a dream as your brain activity progresses to a more awake state

- The heart rate rises to near to its wakeful state

- Your limbs may even become paralyzed

- The breathing often becomes faster and even irregular

DEEP SLEEP REQUIREMENTS

W hile a person needs all of the sleep stages, deep sleep is particularly important for brain health and function. Deep sleep allows the brain to build and store new memories and improves its ability to collect and recall information.

This sleep stage also allows the brain to relax and recover from a day of activity, allowing it to replenish the energy for the next day in the form of glucose.

Deep sleep also plays a part in regulating hormones. During this stage, the pituitary gland secretes human growth hormone, which helps tissues grow and regenerate cells in the body.

Importantly, a person needs to get enough deep sleep to accomplish these functions. The amount of deep sleep a person has is going to contribute to how much total sleep they get. For most adults, sleeping 7-9 hours is the normal recommendation which gives the body plenty of time in the deeper sleeping conditions.

If one day the body does not get enough deep sleep, it can compensate for this the next day by moving rapidly through the cycles reach the deepest stages of sleep and remain there longer.

However, if the person does not get enough deep sleep

regularly, this may begin to affect the brain.

As deep sleep plays a role in memory, if the body does not get enough sleep, it will have difficulty creating new memories or retaining the information.

How to get More Deep Sleep

There might be a few of ways to increase the amount of deep sleep a person gets every night.

As the American Sleep Association says, setting aside more time for sleep is the most important thing a person can do to increase the amount of deep sleep they get each night. Doing so helps the body to go through further stages of sleep, which promotes a deeper sleep.

Other procedures may generally help promote deep sleep and good sleep, such as:

- Exercising vigorously, such as jogging, running, or swimming early in the day rather than before bedtime.

- Make dietary changes which include fewer carbohydrates and healthy fats

- Warm up your body up in a spa or hot sauna

Additionally, some antidepressants may help people get deeper sleep, though this is not the case for everyone.

Pink noise can also make a person's deep sleep more effective. Pink noise is a random noise, with components that are more low-frequency than normal. A research in the journal Frontiers in Human Neuroscience explored the effects on deep sleep by using sound stimulation, such as pink noise. The findings suggested that listening to these sounds could improve the deep sleep state of a person, resulting in better memory function when they wake up.

Some general healthy sleep habits can also help to promote better sleep experience, including:

- Avoid blue lights, such as computers or smartphones near bedtime

- Keep the room as quiet as possible by closing windows and turning off lights on alarm clocks

- Avoiding caffeine later in the day

- Reducing stress

- Avoiding big meals before bedtime

- Set a schedule for sleep and try to fall asleep at the same time every night

Deep sleep is an integral part of the sleep process, but it is just one component of a good night's sleep. There may be several ways to encourage deeper sleep, such as exercising or listening to pink noise while falling asleep.

The best way to get deeper sleep can be as simple as setting side enough time to sleep every night.

What Are the Benefits of Deep Sleep?

During deep sleep, the metabolism of glucose in the brain increases, promoting short- and long-term memory and general learning.

Deep sleep is also when the pituitary gland secretes vital hormones, such as human growth hormone, contributing to growth and body development.

Other benefits of deep sleep include:

- increasing blood supply to muscles

- energy restoration

- cell regeneration

- strengthening the immune system

- promoting growth and repair of tissues and bones

What Happens When You do not get Enough Deep Sleep?

Deep sleep is responsible for helping to process the information that you come across every day. Without enough sleep, the brain cannot commit that information to your memory.

Not getting a good sleep is often related to conditions, such as:

- diabetes

- stroke

- Alzheimer's disease

- heart disease

The deep sleep stage itself is related to certain disorders, like:

- bedwetting

- sleep eating

- sleepwalking

- night terrors

How Much Deep Sleep do You Need?

You spend about 75% of your night in non-REM sleep, and the other 25% in REM sleep. Of this, deep sleep is around 13% to 23% of your total sleep.

Deep sleep diminishes with age. You have two hours of deep sleep each night if you are under 30. If, on the other hand, you are over 65, you may get just half an hour of deep sleep every night, or none at all.

Deep sleep is not necessarily needed, but younger people may need more because it encourages growth and development. Older people often need deep sleep, but not getting much does not necessarily indicate a sleep disorder.

How do You Know How Much You're Getting?

If you wake up feeling tired, this could be an indication that you haven't had enough deep sleep.

Wearable devices at home measure sleep by monitoring the changes in your body during the night. Still, this technology is relatively new. Although it can help to identify the patterns of sleep, it may not be an accurate measure of how much deep sleep you get.

Your doctor may recommend a sleep study known as Polysomnography (PSG). You'll sleep in a laboratory during this test while you're hooked up to monitors that measure:

- body movements

- heart rate

- breathing rate

- oxygen levels

- brain waves

Your doctor can use this information to see if you are reaching deep sleep and other stages throughout the night.

Tips for Better Sleep

The heat will spur more slow- wave sleep. Taking a hot bath or spending time in a sauna before bed, for example, may help improve the quality of your sleep.

Eating a low-carbohydrate diet or taking certain antidepressants may also promote deep sleep, though further research in this area is needed.

Overall, getting enough sleep can increase your deep sleep too.

Here are some tips:

- Set yourself to a bedtime routine where you go to sleep and wake up every day at the same time

- Get plenty of exercises. Every day is a good start, about 20 to 30 minutes, just stop working out in the hours before bedtime

- Stick to water and other decaffeinated drinks before bedtime. Alcohol, caffeine, and nicotine will make having a good night's rest more difficult

- Create a bedtime routine, such as reading a book or taking a bath to relax from the day

- Remove flashing lights from your bedroom and loud noises. Too much time on the TV or computer will make it difficult to relax

- Do not lie tossing and turning in bed. Try doing a light activity, such as reading, until you're exhausted again

- Consider changing your pillows if you've had them for more than a year and find it difficult to get comfortable

DEEP SLEEP: HOW TO GET MORE OF IT

W e already know what deep sleep is, and how our bodies need it to function properly, but what exactly is it? There is a large body of deep sleep research, but we have all the knowledge we need to know about what it is, its purpose and how you can get more of it.

Deep sleep is the stage of sleep that is related to the slowest brain waves during sleep. This period of sleep is known as slow-wave sleep because the EEG activity is characterized by slow waves with a relatively high amplitude and a frequency of less than 1 Hz. A down-state implies the initial portion of the wave; an inhibition period during which the neurons in the neocortex remain silent. It is during this period that the neocortical neurons will relax.

An upstate indicates the next section of the wave; an excitation period during which the neurons fire briefly at a rapid rate. This state is a phase of depolarization, whereas the former state is a phase of hyperpolarization. In comparison to Rapid Eye Movement Sleep (REM sleep cycle), absent or slow eye movement, lack of genital activity, and moderate muscle tone are the main characteristics of slow-wave sleep.

Research Behind Sleep Stages and Deep Sleep

Deep sleep can be defined as stage three of non-rapid eye movement sleep and is often referred to as "slow-wave sleep" according to the 1968 Rechtschaffen & Kales (R & K) Standard. There is no significant distinction between stages three and four; however, stage three has delta activity of 20% to 50%, while stage four has more than 50%. The American Academy of Sleep Medicine has no longer referred to stage four since the year 2008, and stage three and four merged to create stage three. A duration of 30 seconds of sleep, consisting of 20% or more slow-wave sleep, is therefore now called stage three. One of the Stages of Sleep is slow-wave sleep (deep sleep).

Features of Deep Sleep

- High arousal threshold

- Presumed restoration of body and brain

- Electroencephalograph (EEG) demonstrates delta waves (low frequency, high amplitude)

- Consolidation of memories

Why is Deep Sleep Important?

Deep sleep is essential for consolidating new memories and is sometimes referred to as "sleep-dependent memory processing." Therefore, individuals with primary insomnia may have impaired memory consolidation and will not function as effectively as regular patients after a period of sleep. Therefore, slow-wave sleep

380

increases the declarative memory, and this involves both episodic and semantic memory.

A core model was built on the premise that long-term memory storage is facilitated by interaction between the neocortical and hippocampal networks. Several studies indicate that there was a substantially higher density of human sleep spindles as compared to the non-learning control task until subjects were conditioned to learn a declarative memory task. It is due to unconscious wave oscillations, which make up the intracellular recordings from thalamic and cortical neurons.

Function of Deep Sleep

Studies of human sleep deprivation seem to indicate that the primary function of deep sleep may be to allow the brain time to recover from its everyday operation. The increase in the metabolism of glucose in the brain is attributed to activities involving mental activity. Another feature affected by slow-wave sleep is the release of the growth hormone, which at this point is at its highest. This also causes an increase in parasympathetic neural activity as well as a decline in sympathetic neural activity.

The highest arousal thresholds are observed in deep sleep, such as the intensity of being disturbed by the sound of a specific volume. When a person wakes up from slow-wave sleep, they are usually not very alert. Cognitive tests after awakening does indicate that mental performance can be impaired for periods of up to 30 minutes as compared to other stage awakenings. This phenomenon is called "sleep inertia."

After sleep deprivation, there is often a fast recovery of slow-wave sleep, meaning that the next bout of sleep will involve not only more slow-wave sleep than normal but deeper slow-wave sleep. In addition to the duration of sleepless period, the preceding duration of this stage will decide the duration of slow-wave sleep. The key factor to consider when determining the amount of slow-wave sleep in any given sleep period is the length of the preceding sleeplessness, which is usually correlated with the build-up of sleep-inducing substances in the brain.

Sleep Disorders During Deep Sleep

There are many sleep disorders and parasomnia that often occur during slow-wave sleep. Sleepwalking (Somnambulism), bed-wetting (Enuresis), sexsomnia, night terrors, and sleep eating are all associated with slow-wave sleep. People with narcolepsy often have fragmented deep sleep.

Factors that Increase Slow-Wave Deep Sleep

Severe prolonged exercise and body heating, such as immersion in a sauna or hot tub, are factors which have shown to improve slow-wave sleep during the sleep period that follows.

Studies have shown that slow-wave sleep is induced when the temperature of the brain reaches a certain threshold. It's believed that this threshold is regulated by circadian rhythm and homeostatic processes. An exceptionally low, short-term carbohydrates diet in healthy sleepers causes an increase in the percentage of slow-wave sleep. This involves an increase in the percentage of dreaming sleep (REM sleep) compared to a mixed diet regime. It is thought that these changes in sleep could very well be linked to the metabolism of the fat content in a low carbohydrate diet.

Additionally, ingestion of antidepressants and certain SSRI's can increase the duration of slow-wave sleep periods; however, THC's effects on slow-wave sleep remain controversial. In such cases, overall sleep time is always unchanged because of the alarm clock, circadian rhythms, or early morning commitments of a person.

How to Get More Deep Sleep

The most important thing you can do to increase your amount of deep sleep is to give yourself more total time to sleep. Individuals may also deprive themselves of complete sleep. REM sleep is also reduced, in addition to decreasing deep sleep.

Some data suggest that intense exercise can improve or stabilize deep sleep. Some sleeping specialists recommend aerobic activities such as running, swimming, and jogging. It is better for those who are prone to insomnia to work out earlier in the day and not before bedtime.

Stage three of the stages of the sleep cycle, slow-wave sleep (deep sleep), is an important part of the cognitive function. It plays an essential part in consolidating memory and rebuilding the brain.

Because of its value to your overall health, you have to increase your amount of deep sleep by allowing you to have enough total nightly sleep time. In addition, exercise and a balanced diet are different approaches that you can use to help make your slow-wave sleep better.

HOW TO INCREASE DEEP SLEEP

If you find yourself having the necessary nighttime hours of sleep but still thinking your body hasn't rejuvenated itself, you probably aren't getting enough deep sleep. This stage of sleep is responsible for healing and rebuilding the body, replenishing cells and revitalizing the immune system, as opposed to light sleep. It's a critical rest stage, but we often don't get enough of it. Deep sleep will make up about 10-20 percent of your entire night's rest. The first cycle of deep sleep lasts 45 to 90 minutes, and from there each subsequent cycle gets shorter.

If you wake up feeling exhausted after 7 to 9 hours of sleep, there are a few steps you can take to improve your time in deep sleep.

HOW TO INCREASE DEEP SLEEP

- **Keep Your Diet Sleep-Friendly**

The American Sleep Association found that, relative to those who eat a mixed diet, a low carbohydrate diet causes an improvement in deep sleep time. There's also a growing body of evidence suggesting that drinking bitter cherry juice will help

384

increase the time spent in deep sleep.

- **Try Pink Noise**

A recent Northwestern Medicine study found that pink noise, such as waves lapping on a beach or trees rustling in the wind, increased the amount of time spent in deep sleep. While it only studied 13 people, it's an exciting exploration of sleep solutions in the world. There are some great sound machines that feature every sound variety, including pink noise. Give one a try and see if your deep sleep improves.

- **Hypnosis Before Bed**

A 2014 study by the University of Fribourg in Switzerland found that subjects listening to sleep-promoting audio recordings of hypnotic suggestions spent as much as 80% more time in deep sleep compared to those not listening to the recordings. There are both free and paid audio resources offering a form of hypnosis and using one might help with your deep sleep deficit.

- **Get the Right Amount of Exercise**

The National Health Institutes suggest about 30 minutes of exercise a day, 5 days a week. That's right at the sweet spot between what's best for deep sleep enhancement and your overall sleep quality. Try not to overdo it though, too much physical activity can often lead to sleep problems or even insomnia. Try something you enjoy doing for the 30-minute average per day. Fortunately, you don't have to become a cross-country sprinter or a cross-fit junkie to work out for better sleep. Easy exercise such as walking the dog, light jogging and even yoga can do the trick as well. It takes good sleep to find the energy you need to exercise every day.

- **Listen to ASMR Videos**

Have you heard of ASMR? A 2015 study defined it as, "Autonomous Sensory Meridian Response in which individuals experience a tingling, static-like sensation across the scalp, back of the neck and at times additional areas in response to specific audio and visual stimuli. It is widely reported that this sensation is accompanied by feelings of relaxation and well-being. "This study found that 82% of respondents used ASMR to help them sleep, and 70% used it to manage stress. There's a wide number of ASMR vloggers out there, and each caters for different ASMR triggers."

You can get the deep sleep your body requires to recover your strength, muscles and physical well-being through exercise, a healthy diet and some other new tricks. Try out these ideas and see what works tonight for you!

CHAPTER 10
CALM YOUR MIND

L ife constantly throws chaos at us — whether it's our relationships, our finances, or our health. In the world of work, around 50% of people are burned out in industries such as banking, and health care, and employers spend $300 billion a year on stress related issues in the workplace.

We just keep moving through, surviving on adrenaline, in response. We overschedule ourselves; we're drinking another coffee; we're responding to another post. When we stay hyperactive all the time, we believe that ultimately, we will get things done.

But all that does is burn us out, drain our productivity, and make us exhaust ourselves.

There is another way — a more relaxed way. Cultivating a more comfortable and confident state of mind does not mean we are going to sink in all of our responsibilities. Research suggests that tackling them would get us more attention, creativity, and energy, and research also points to easy ways we can tap into the peaceful state of mind in our stressful lives to be more resilient.

A STRESSED MIND VS. A CALM MIND

Stress was never meant to be a 24/7 experience. As Stanford professor Robert Sapolsky states, in the five minutes just before you die, you are just expected to feel depressed. If a wild animal chases you in the savanna, your reaction to stress is supposed to save your life — it mobilizes your energy, your muscles and your immune system to get you out of danger quickly. When animals flee, they come into the "rest-and-digest" state after the fight-or-flight state, where the parasympathetic nervous system is working to replenish their energy.

The stress response should be short-lived because it is wearing down your body, health and energy. It also influences things like your emotional outlook and the way you make decisions. You are more likely to react to situations when you are stressed than to answer with reason.

You perceive the world differently, too. Stress makes us fractious, and we cannot see the bigger picture. Our focus gets wider when we're calmer, we really see more things. Participants in one study completed a three-month meditation session.

They then engaged in something called the attentional blink task, in which you watch photos appear quickly one after the other. If people do this exercise, their mind usually doesn't pick up all the target pictures. However, after the training in meditation, participants were able to pick up more of the target images than pre-treatment — suggesting their state of mind had become more attentive.

Being able to show greater attention means you know more about other people and can interact more easily with them. For an evolutionary reason, high stress and anxiety (or any form of negative emotion) make us self-focused: when our ancestors were stressed, it was because they were in a situation of survival. It was good to concentrate on yourself, so you can save your life.

If we're stressed, we're less likely to notice if a friend looks burned out or depressed, and more likely to get annoyed if they're not doing as we expect. But when you're in a calmer and happier place, it's probably the day you're going to have more empathy: you're going to notice your colleague and take the time to reach out and ask if you can do anything to support them.

You can control your energy when you are calm because you are not constantly burning yourself out, spending your days in overdrive with your sympathetic nervous system. Calm lets you concentrate on what you need to do and get it done quickly.

Calmness can also influence your creativity. Research shows that when we're not actively concentrating or stressed, our most creative thoughts come in moments. When our brain is in alpha wave mode, which is a relaxed state of mind, we are at our most creative — like when you are in the shower or taking a stroll in nature. People who go four days on an immersive nature retreat come back with creativity increased by 50 percent.

If you want to make the most of yourself in terms of

productivity, innovation, and creativity — making progress at work or just addressing the simple life issues you face — calm is the key.

How to Cultivate a Calm State of Mind

We do know how to get stressed. Many of us are excellent at stimulating and overloading our adrenal system. The problem then is, how do you wind down? Research suggests some behaviors that not only feel good but also place us in a calmer, more comfortable state — a state from which we are better able to cope with whatever life throws at us.

1. Breathing

Jake, who appears in the book The Happiness Track, was an American Marine officer in charge of a Humvee on a convoy through Afghanistan, as he was driving his vehicle passed over an improvised explosive device. He looked down after the blast and found his legs badly broken below the knee. In that moment of surprise, panic and pain, he recalled a breathing exercise he had read about for situations of intense wartime.

It allowed him to fulfil his duty, which was to inspect everyone else in the vehicle. It gave him the presence of mind to issue instructions for help, and then to tourniquet his own legs and support them until he fell unconscious — that saved his life.

Our breathing is an effective way of controlling our emotions and we take it for granted. Through your breath, you can activate your parasympathetic nervous system -the calming response in your body.

That's why we switched to breathing to help veterans—50% of whom see little improvement from therapy or treatment for their trauma symptoms. The veterans were doubtful but we started teaching them various exercises in breathing. Some of them began sleeping without medication within a couple of days; after the week-long program, many of them no longer qualified as having post-traumatic stress, and that persisted until a year later.

You can change how you feel by using your breathing. Researchers observed people experiencing various emotions in another study, and noticed there was a different breathing pattern for each. We then gave the various breathing patterns to other people to follow, and asked them, "How do you feel? "It turned out that relaxation exercises actually evoked the emotions.

One of the most calming breathing exercises you can do is breathe in (for example, to a count of four), hold and then breathe out for up to twice as long (for example, to a count of six or eight). You should gently close your mouth, making a sound like the ocean, which is used to breathe deep relaxation. As you do this, especially thanks to those long exhalations you stimulate the parasympathetic nervous system, reducing your blood pressure and heart rate.

2. Self-compassion

We are our worst critic. We claim that being self-critical can help us become more self-conscious and make us work harder, but this is a fallacy. Indeed, according to much study, self-criticism is undermining our resilience. When we criticize ourselves , we are less likely to learn from our mistakes. Self-critical people tend to be more depressed and anxious, and unable to bounce back from the struggles.

Imagine someone running a marathon in their life for the very first time, and they trip and fall. On the sidelines, someone says, "You are a loser, you are not a runner. What is it you are doing here? Go home. "That person is the voice of our inner self-criticism. On the other hand, self-compassion is someone who says, "everybody falls, that's normal. You are so amazing; you are absolutely killing this.

Self-compassion is the ability to be mindful of your emotions — conscious of the emotions going on inside if you fail at anything. It doesn't mean you identify with them; you can simply watch them and note them without feeding the flames. Self-compassion also involves understanding that mistakes are made by everyone and that it is part of being human. And, it's the opportunity to say to yourself exactly the way you'd speak to a friend who failed, kindly and warmly.

Research shows that when we follow this way of thinking, we are calmer — we have less feelings of tension and lower levels of cortisol. We're much more resilient: We're less afraid of failure and more motivated to get better.

3. **Connection**

How often are we really 100% there for another person? When was the last time anyone, including your partner, was 100 percent there with you?

There is an epidemic of loneliness in the USA and around the world. We know these feelings of loneliness are extremely destructive to our mind and body, leading to poorer health and even earlier death. The tensions and lack of peace in the world today can add to this loneliness because of the way it tends to make us self-centered.

After food and shelter, our greatest human need is to connect with others in a positive way. We have a deep and profound desire to belong to one another from the moment we are born until our last day. And when we meet that need, it brings us calm: The oxytocin and natural opioids we release when we connect can exert a calming influence on our bodies, and the knowledge that we have the support of others can soothe our minds. Research suggests that when we face adversity, our relationships and our community have a part to play in our resilience.

So how do we build a state of mind where we feel more connected?

The good news is that you can turn your focus outward and feel more connected by taking care of yourself and your own well-being through activities such as breathing and self-compassion. Positive feelings such as calm, of course, help us feel closer to others. You may also try different practices that research has found to improve your sense of connection.

4. Compassion for others

Imagine a day where things will not go well for you — you have spilled your coffee on yourself, and it's raining, and then a friend calls who has a real problem in their life, and you get up and go quickly to help them. What's happens to your state of mind in that moment?

All of a sudden, you have a lot of energy; you are at their disposal. That's what practicing compassion, altruism, and service does to your life.

It increases your well-being tremendously as many of us have experienced little acts of kindness when we act in this way. Our heart rate goes down when we feel compassion and our parasympathetic nervous system gets more activated.

Compassion and kindness can help to protect us from adversity as well. Researchers have found in one of my favorite studies that people who had endured stressful life situations had a shorter lifespan.

But there was a small group of people among those participants who just seemed to keep on living. What'd happened to these people?

When the researchers dug a little deeper, they found that they were all involved in helping friends and relatives in their lives — from assisting with transportation or shopping to housework and child care. Service is one of the deepest ways of nurturing the community around you but also of nurturing, inspiring and energizing yourself. It's like that children's book — when you fill somebody's bucket, it fills up yours too.

Cultivating calmness is not about suppressing all kinds of unpleasant emotions. In fact, when we make time to breathe, connect and care, some of the negative feelings we've been running from could catch up with us. But this is the time of self-compassion; it is all right to feel bad. Resilience doesn't mean we're going to be happy all the time, but it does mean we have the mindset, the energy, and other people's support to help us weather the storm.

CHAPTER 11
HOW QUITTING SMOKING HAS CHANGED MY LIFE

Years of smoking ingrains behaviors and patterns of thought which are more about addiction than our true feelings and preferences.

Once we stop smoking, we are often surprised at changes in attitude toward smoking and life in general.

Steve, a member of DelphiForums About Smoking Cessation support group, recently gathered some new (and some not-so-new) ex-smokers to discuss how smoking cessation has changed their way of thinking and acting.

Their responses are posted below; But first, the question from Steve and then a glimpse into how smoking cessation impacts our lives positively.

From Steve:

"When we smoked, we had a certain mentality. When we quit and obtained our freedom from addiction, our mentality changed. What's the biggest change or transformation in thought that you've experienced since you quit smoking?"

Transformations Brought on By Quitting

• "After I quit, I began to understand how much I really didn't like it! I haven't become that bad an ex-smoker, but give me a couple more years!" ~ Steve

• "At the end of 10 months, I am now more optimistic and more careful in my thinking. When I make a decision, I take my time to think about all the possibilities. I feel better in my resolve to stay a non-smoker, as well. It amazes me how proud I am of my ability to finally feel that I will remain a non-smoker. I never really believed I could do this after 44 years of smoking. My thinking has been changed forever." ~Deb

• "I think I'm more concerned about myself now: my health, I'm standing up for myself when necessary, I feel like there are more possibilities out there without my smoking monkey on my back." ~ Linda

• "I learned that I don't need cigarettes to know when I'm sad, happy, anxious, bored, stressed, surprised, angry, impatient, nervous, confused, scared, lost, or any other emotion. The only thing I did was to temporarily reduce the symptoms of withdrawal from nicotine and hide my emotions behind a veil of smoke." ~Jenn

• "I'm now a different person than I was on Feb. 28, 2013. I'm more aware of what I'm eating since I quit smoking. I lead a healthier lifestyle. I'm a more kind, thoughtful, and patient person than when I was smoking. I like who I've become rather than the person who was ruled by a cigarette ... I'm so happy to be on the other side ... I'm happy." ~Gail

• "The reality checks after I read on the NRT patches that patch exposure can destroy small household pets and kids. Something so deadly, without even a flame, blows my mind. When I walk or walk around the property, I'm taking small trash bags with me now to try to clean up after litterers (straw as well as cigarette butts). It's amazing how throwing a filter into water can kill a fish, a salamander, and other small aquatic wildlife. When I'm feeling healthy and can get out and about, I guess I have kind of made it my mission to stop others from hurting wildlife that did not choose to smoke or come into contact with poison." ~Rose

• "I've been leading a busy life. I've never had time to smoke because of all the smoke time I wanted. Now, I can "do" stuff, and I don't have to sit down and smoke away while I think about it. I still delay to some extent ... but it's a lot better." ~Vivienne

• "Quitting smoking changed me in a lot of ways, but I believe the enhanced empathy, the willingness to put myself in someone else's shoes was a big one. One of my favorite quotes from Maya Angelou is proven day after day: "I've learned that people will forget what you've said, people will forget what you've done, but people can never forget how you've made them" ~Dee

• "I'm a new quitter. I've been nicotine-free for 24 days! I've noticed changes in my outlook in this short time. I find myself more confident —- like if I can quit smoking, I can accomplish other things I may have thought impossible! This fresh feeling is a lovely and unexpected surprise." ~Mmac

• "I've walked through so many transformations in the past [smoke-free] 8 months, and I'm sure I'm going to keep changing a few more times, but today I feel confident in myself, and I feel grateful for finding such a great group of people to get me here. The anger, fear, and confusion I had at the beginning of my journey is gone-Hallelujah!" ~Peggy

• "I think one improvement for me was seeking comfort in solitude. Instead of taking drags on a cigarette, I'm enjoying the peace and relaxation of deep breaths. I'm seeing clearly instead of a cloud of smoke, and I've gained more patience." ~Andrea

• "The change seems to be evolving for me. I guess this evolution first became apparent to me about the sixth months after quitting smoking. I suddenly wasn't depressed anymore, and I figured this was because my brain had adjusted for the first time in 35 years to have a normal dopamine level."

• "The second indication of the change was when I discovered that I could get a level of inner peace when I breathed deeply at around the tenth month, and it's getting better. I never felt better, physically in my life. I don't want to sound too arrogant, but I can't even look at a pack of cigs anymore without seeing them as a poison I don't want to have any part of."

• "But I want to stay on this journey more than anything else to see how much better it can actually get." ~Rick

As smokers, most of us feel that stopping smoking makes life dull and less satisfying. Cigarettes are with us all day, every day. The idea that we do not have them triggers fear in our hearts.

The truth of life without smoke is quite the opposite. When we start overcoming nicotine addiction, the benefits that we didn't expect start showing, and we can settle comfortably into our new lives. It doesn't happen immediately, but it will happen if you allow yourself the time and space required to recover from this addiction

Do not let fear of life stop you from getting started with smoking cessation. The benefits shot outweigh the discomforts.

TOM USED HYPNOSIS TO STOP SMOKING

I really wanted to quit smoking, but I couldn't.

I smoked for twenty years, starting my late teens, which I now remember as especially stupid because I was a competitive athlete (in soccer) at the time I started my habit. I have taught abroad for most of my adult life, and many of the countries I lived in (especially parts of Europe and Asia) were more open to public smoking than America is. When I returned home, I found that I was no longer able to smoke in restaurants, in homes of other people, and in other places where I had become used to lighting up, and I felt alone. Smoking has always aggravated my asthma, and I knew of course that it's very deadly too. But I just couldn't stop.

I have tried cold turkey (which worked several times, once for two years), nicotine gum, wellbutrin, and a nicotine patch to quit in the past. And about six months ago, I was on depression and alcohol abuse treatment, and my doctor suggested attempting to stop smoking using therapeutic hypnosis. As I decided to stay away from some sort of chemical treatment (such as anti-depressants, or even therapies based on nicotine), I was interested. I kind of felt like, why not?

I found hypnosis surprisingly accessible, and not weird. This felt to me like a combination of a relaxation treatment and a counseling session. I felt very relaxed but not "out of it," as in movies. I felt that I was present. I think that's helped cut me down. I haven't stopped, just about half of what I used to smoke. Smoking to me now is not an automatic response. Hypnosis seems to have made me calmer, or at least more aware that I have a choice.

I found my hypnotherapist through my counselor on chemical addictions. I don't know if my psychologist, or my regular doctor who I see for asthma, would have suggested hypnosis. However, they did not speak out against it. I guess they're just glad to see people trying to stop smoking in whatever way they can!

I felt that some people thought it was strange, a kind of "magical thinking," but none of my practitioners advised against it, and most people were really interested in knowing more about it once you started talking about it.

I'd say hypnosis isn't for everybody, but it's definitely worth trying. I know it can't hurt, and really could help, so why not? I feel the same about other holistic therapies: when I was in Asia, I tried acupuncture and massage therapy, and both helped me with various health issues, including asthma to anxiety

CONCLUSION

Smoking cigarettes is the greatest single cause of illness and premature death in the US. The number is far bigger worldwide. Every year, tobacco kills about seven million people, although about one million deaths are due to exposure to second-hand smoke by non-smokers.

Although nearly 80,000 people in the US die each year from smoking-related illnesses, one in five adults are still regular smokers.

Now things appear to be changing. Forty years ago, 51 percent of males and 41 percent of females were smokers. Those rates have dropped by more than half, with 15% of adults in the U.S. smoking, and 59% claiming they never smoked.

Quitting smoking is one of the biggest challenges a person faces, and often they need more than just willpower. A lot of options are available now; from campaigns like Stoptober and local community groups to medications. Hypnotherapy provides an attractive solution for many people.

Self-hypnosis can be used to help you achieve meaningful changes in your life, such as stopping smoking. Find your session time and place – make sure it's quiet enough so you won't be interrupted.

Lie or sit down and close your eyes. Take three slow, deep breaths, keep the third breath in for three seconds. Then as you breathe out, relax and sink back into your seat. Focus on your breathing, and let your thoughts flow in and out as if attached to your breath until you have cleared your mind.

Now count backwards from 10 to 0, counting each number as you breathe out and focusing on another area of your body, enabling it to relax. I begin with my toes and work up to my head, but you can try head down to your feet, you prefer to do so. Whichever works.

You're going to be relaxed at this point, but to help deepen that relaxation, imagine yourself in a quiet place. I like using the beach: Picture the beach in as much detail as possible. If you hate beaches, try to imagine a meadow or garden, wherever you feel most relaxed.

Now you are in that state of concentration and relaxation; you can make a suggestion to yourself, feel more confident about quitting smoking, or visualize your reason for quitting more vividly so that you feel increasing motivation to achieve your goal. It is your time, so make wise use of it.

Once it's time to wake up, just count yourself back from 0 all the way up to ten and you will find yourself wide awake, feeling refreshed and re-energized. If for whatever reason, you need to be fully awake and ready during your session, you're going to be, and can automatically bring yourself awake. That's it! It's really that easy to start making meaningful life changes."

If you enjoyed this book, please let me know your thoughts by leaving a short review on Audible... Thank you

9 781801 766098